COMPLETE
EnglishSmart®

GRADE **5**

| Section 1 | **Listening Comprehension** |

Unit 1 6 – 9
Treasures of the Orient

Unit 2 10 – 13
Pirates of the Caribbean

Unit 3 14 – 17
Mae Jemison – a Great Inspiration

Unit 4 18 – 21
Bicycles – Then and Now

Unit 5 22 – 25
Meat-eating Plants

Review 1 26 – 31

| Section 2 | **Grammar** |

Unit 1 34 – 37
Nouns

Unit 2 38 – 41
Direct and Indirect Objects

Unit 3 42 – 45
Pronouns

Unit 4 46 – 49
Modal Verbs

Unit 5 50 – 53
Simple and Progressive Tenses

Unit 6 54 – 57
Perfect Tenses

Unit 7 58 – 61
Active and Passive Voice

Unit 8 62 – 65
Direct and Indirect Speech

Unit 9 66 – 69
Adjectives

Unit 10 70 – 73
Adverbs

Unit 11 74 – 77
Phrases

Unit 12 78 – 81
Clauses

Unit 13 82 – 85
Sentences

Unit 14 86 – 89
Punctuation

Review 2 90 – 95

| Section 3 | **Vocabulary** |

Unit 1 98 – 101
Nature Words

Unit 2 102 – 105
Fire Words

Unit 3 106 – 109
Sport Words

Unit 4 110 – 113
Personality Trait Words

Unit 5 114 – 117
Disaster Words

Contents

Unit 6   118 – 121
Astronomy Words

Unit 7   122 – 125
Feeling Words

Unit 8   126 – 129
Feline Words

Unit 9   130 – 133
Animal Words

Unit 10   134 – 137
Medical Words

Unit 11   138 – 141
Archaeology Words

Unit 12   142 – 145
Communication Words

Unit 13   146 – 149
Genre Words

Unit 14   150 – 153
Fashion Words

Review 3   154 – 159

Section 4   Reading and Writing

Unit 1   162 – 165
Fortune Telling Newspaper

Unit 2   166 – 169
The Myth of Daedalus and
Icarus

Unit 3   170 – 173
Aladdin

Unit 4   174 – 177
Power for Sale

Unit 5   178 – 181
Summer List

Unit 6   182 – 185
Marilyn Bell

Unit 7   186 – 189
The History of the Canadian
Flag

Unit 8   190 – 193
Think Big!

Unit 9   194 – 197
The Amazing Helen Keller

Unit 10   198 – 201
Bigfoot Sighting

Unit 11   202 – 205
The Volcano

Unit 12   206 – 209
Canada's Minimum Wage

Unit 13   210 – 213
I Can't Play

Unit 14   214 – 217
Sunrise Paradise

Review 4   218 – 223

Listening Scripts   225 – 230

Answers   231 – 256

Language Games   257 – 272

Dear Parent,

Thank you for choosing our *Complete EnglishSmart* as your child's learning companion.

We are confident that *Complete EnglishSmart* is the ultimate supplementary workbook your child needs to build his or her English language skills.

Complete EnglishSmart explores the fundamental aspects of language development – listening comprehension, grammar, vocabulary, reading, and writing – by introducing each concept with an easy-to-understand definition and clear examples. This is followed by a variety of interesting activities to provide plenty of practice for your child. There is also a note box at the end of each unit for your child to note down what he or she has learned.

To further ensure that your child retains the language concepts and enjoys the material, there is a review at the end of each section and a Language Games section at the end of the book to help your child consolidate the language concepts in a fun and meaningful way. The accompanying online audio clips (www.popularbook.ca/downloadcentre) let your child practise and develop his or her listening skills.

If your child would like to show his or her understanding of the language concepts in a creative way, we are happy to invite your child on a bonus Language Game Design Challenge. Please find the detailed information on page 271 of this book.

We hope that your child will have fun learning and developing his or her English language skills with our *Complete EnglishSmart*.

Your Partner in Education,
Popular Book Company (Canada) Limited

Don't forget to participate in our
Language Game Design Challenge *on p. 271 for your chance to win a prize!*

Section 1

Listening Comprehension

Scan this QR Code or go to Download Centre at
www.popularbook.ca for audio clips.

UNIT 1

Treasures of the Orient

 This passage explains the events that led to the discovery of a new trade route between Europe and Asia and the significant parts played by the Polo family and Kublai Khan.

1.1 Read the questions in this unit before listening. Take notes as you listen. You may read the listening script on page 225 if needed.

Keywords	Notes
century	
channelled	
Silk Route	
Constantinople	
Mediterranean	
European	
Venice	
Kublai Khan	
Asia Minor	
Persia	
Afghanistan	
Himalayan	
Gobi	
Shangdu	
Orient	

A. Read the questions. Then check the correct answers.

1. What was Kublai Khan interested in?

Ⓐ the European culture

Ⓑ merchants from Venice

Ⓒ the Polo family

Ⓓ a four-year journey

2. In which year did the Polo family set out for China?

Ⓐ 1270

Ⓑ 1217

Ⓒ 1279

Ⓓ 1271

3. What was the final destination of the Polo family?

Ⓐ Afghanistan

Ⓑ the Himalayan mountains

Ⓒ China

Ⓓ the Gobi Desert

4. How long did the Polos stay in China?

Ⓐ for 70 years

Ⓑ for 17 years

Ⓒ for 17 days

Ⓓ for 17 months

B. Listen to the questions and answer options. Then write the correct letters in the boxes.

1.2 ❶ ❷ ❸ ❹

C.   Fill in the blanks with the correct words to complete the sentences.

1.   In the 13th century, trade between Europe and Asia was channelled through the _____ .

2.   The European merchants wanted the _____ , spices, and _____ found in the East.

3.   _____ was the name of the Chinese ruler.

4.   Present-day Iran and Iraq were known as _____ .

5.
Present-day Beijing was known as _____ .

D.   Answer the questions.

1.   Why was a new trade route needed?

_____

_____

2.   Which areas did the Polo family travel through?

_____

_____

_____

3.   What lessons do you think the Polo family learned on their journey?

_____

_____

_____

E. Listen to the passage "Treasures of the Orient" again. Then write a summary in no more than 80 words.

1.1

> Include only the main points in the summary. Use your own words.

Summary

_____

_____

_____

_____

_____

_____

_____

_____

_____

Words that I Have Learned

_____

_____

_____

_____

UNIT 2 Pirates of the Caribbean

 This passage explains how pirates such as Blackbeard gained notoriety for pirating throughout the Caribbean and parts of North America, and the steps taken by the Governor of Virginia to end piracy.

2.1 Read the questions in this unit before listening. Take notes as you listen. You may read the listening script on page 226 if needed.

Keywords	Notes
buccaneer	
legendary	
ruthlessness	
notorious	
fuse	
opponent	
reputation	
Carolina	
governor	
naval officer	
Maynard	
challenge	
inlet	
fatal	
paltry	

A.   Read the questions. Then check the correct answers.

1.   What did Blackbeard put in his hair?

(A) few

(B) fuses

(C) flames

(D) fumes

2.   What was easy for Blackbeard?

(A) parody

(B) policing

(C) privacy

(D) piracy

3.   Who was the Governor of Virginia?

(A) Maynard

(B) Edward Teach

(C) Alexander Spotswood

(D) Henry Morgan

4.   How many members were there in Maynard's crew?

(A) 6

(B) 16

(C) 60

(D) 61

B.   Listen to the questions and answer options. Then write the correct letters in the boxes.

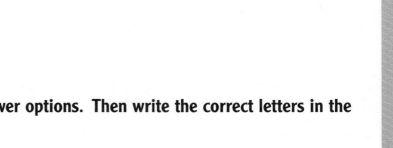

2.2   ❶ ____   ❷ ____   ❸ ____   ❹ ____

C.   Write "T" for the true statements and "F" for the false ones.

1.   Captain Henry Morgan was a pirate.   _____

2.   Piracy was prevalent off the northern coast of
       North America.   _____

3.   Blackbeard was kind to his crew members.   _____

4.   It was expensive to do business in the Caribbean
       and the Carolina coast because of piracy.   _____

5.   The reward for capturing Blackbeard was roughly
       ten years' wages for a captain.   _____

6.   Maynard was a British naval officer.   _____

7.   Maynard captured Blackbeard in the end.   _____

8.   The governor gave Maynard a reward of £100.   _____

D.   Answer the questions.

1.   Describe Blackbeard's physical appearance.

       _____

       _____

       _____

       _____

2.   Why was the actual reward for capturing Blackbeard not worth Maynard
       and his crew risking their lives?

       _____

       _____

       _____

E. **Listen to the passage "Pirates of the Caribbean" again. Then write a summary in no more than 80 words.**

Include only the main points in the summary. Use your own words.

Summary

_____

_____

_____

_____

_____

_____

_____

_____

_____

Words that I Have Learned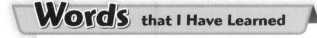

_____

_____

_____

_____

UNIT

3 Mae Jemison – a Great Inspiration

This passage is about the life of Mae C. Jemison. You will learn how she worked hard to become the first African-American woman to go into space, her personal and professional achievements, and her contribution to society.

3.1 Read the questions in this unit before listening. Take notes as you listen. You may read the listening script on page 227 if needed.

Keywords	Notes
accomplishment	
perseverance	
anthropology	
archaeology	
astronomy	
engineering	
aeronautics	
Endeavour	
Mission Specialist	
compassionate	
Cambodian	
refugee	
Peace Corps	
Swahili	
stimulate	

A. **Read the questions. Then check the correct answers.**

1. When was Jemison born?

   (A) October 7, 1956

   (B) October 17, 1956

   (C) September 12, 1956

   (D) September 20, 1956

2. What were some of Jemison's interests?

   (A) anthropology and astronomy

   (B) astronomy and mathematics

   (C) mathematics and biology

   (D) astronomy and biology

3. How long did Mae Jemison's first space mission last?

   (A) eight days

   (B) eight weeks

   (C) eight months

   (D) eight years

4. Where did Jemison provide medical service?

   (A) in Canada

   (B) in Cambodia

   (C) in Russia

   (D) in Japan

B. **Listen to the questions and answer options. Then write the correct letters in the boxes.**

3.2   ①   ②   ③   ④

C.   Complete the timeline.

Mae Jemison's Timeline

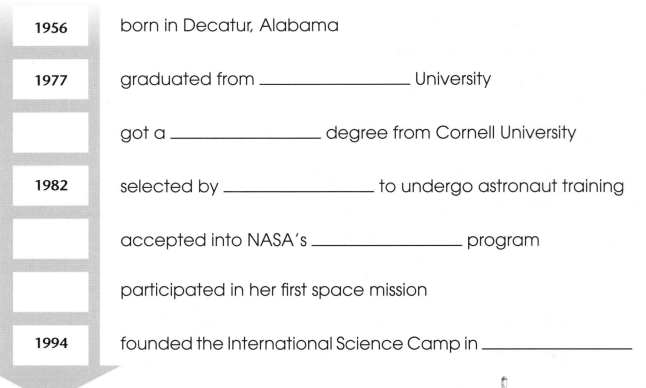

1956	born in Decatur, Alabama
1977	graduated from _____ University
	got a _____ degree from Cornell University
1982	selected by _____ to undergo astronaut training
	accepted into NASA's _____ program
	participated in her first space mission
1994	founded the International Science Camp in _____

D.   Answer the questions.

1.   Describe Jemison's first space mission.

    _____

    _____

    _____

    _____

2.   Write details to support the statement, "Jemison is a compassionate person."

    _____

    _____

    _____

E. **Listen to the passage "Mae Jemison – a Great Inspiration" again. Then write a summary in no more than 80 words.**

3.1

Include only the main points in the summary. Use your own words.

Summary

_____

_____

_____

_____

_____

_____

_____

_____

_____

Words that I Have Learned

_____

_____

_____

_____

UNIT

4 Bicycles – Then and Now

This passage explains the events and modifications that led to the advancement of the original bicycle to the modern bicycle and the reasons behind the renewed interest in cycling.

4.1 Read the questions in this unit before listening. Take notes as you listen. You may read the listening script on page 228 if needed.

Keywords	Notes
Tour de France	
durable	
mechanical	
Pierre Michaux	
mass-marketed	
propulsion	
velocipede	
advancement	
chainwheels	
principle	
volition	
ratio	
sprocket	
cogwheel	
derailleur	

A.   Read the questions. Then check the correct answers.

1.   Which characteristic describes the modern bicycle?

   (A) slow

   (B) uncomfortable

   (C) simple

   (D) durable

2.   What did the "velocipede" resemble?

   (A) a bicycle

   (B) a tricycle

   (C) a motorcycle

   (D) a unicycle

3.   Which model introduced the use of the chain?

   (A) the safety bicycle

   (B) the original bicycle

   (C) the modern bicycle

   (D) the velocipede

4.   What led to a renewed interest in biking?

   (A) environmental concerns

   (B) biological concerns

   (C) medical concerns

   (D) economic concerns

B.   Listen to the questions and answer options. Then write the correct letters in the boxes.

4.2   **1** [ ]   **2** [ ]   **3** [ ]   **4** [ ]

C.   Draw lines to match the facts.

Facts about Bicycles

1.   19th century   •   •   shifts the chain

2.   1887   •   •   the safety bicycle was designed

3.   32 teeth   •   •   the ratio of gears

4.   8 teeth   •   •   the first bicycle appeared

5.   4 to 1   •   •   the rear sprocket

6.   derailleur   •   •   the front chainwheel

D.   Answer the questions.

1.   How were original bicycles different from the modern bicycle?

_____

_____

2.   Why were gears added to the safety bicycle?

_____

_____

_____

3.   Suggest three benefits of cycling.

_____

_____

_____

E. **Listen to the passage "Bicycles – Then and Now" again. Then write a summary in no more than 80 words.**

4.1

Include only the main points in the summary. Use your own words.

Summary

_____

_____

_____

_____

_____

_____

_____

_____

_____

Words that I Have Learned

_____

_____

_____

_____

UNIT 5 Meat-eating Plants

 This passage explains the different types of meat-eating plants such as the Venus Flytrap and the Cobra Lily, and the tactics they use to lure and consume unsuspecting insects.

5.1 Read the questions in this unit before listening. Take notes as you listen. You may read the listening script on page 229 if needed.

Keywords	Notes
adornment	
carnivorous	
notion	
absurd	
unsuspecting	
dietary supplement	
lure	
lobe	
bristle	
secrete	
enzyme	
digestion	
exoskeleton	
devoured	

A. **Read the questions. Then check the correct answers.**

1. What do most plants feed on?

   (A) sunlight and water

   (B) meat and leaves

   (C) animals and insects

   (D) sunlight and fruits

2. How many types of meat-eating plants are there?

   (A) one

   (B) two

   (C) three

   (D) four

3. What is the Cobra Lily named for?

   (A) its flower-like appearance

   (B) its plant-like appearance

   (C) its snake-like appearance

   (D) its insect-like appearance

4. What helps the Venus Flytrap digest insects?

   (A) sunlight and water

   (B) acids and nectar

   (C) enzymes and nectar

   (D) enzymes and acids

B. **Listen to the questions and answer options. Then write the correct letters in the boxes.**

5.2   1   2   3   4

C.   Fill in the blanks with the correct words to complete the sentences.

Some plants are 1._____ , that is, they eat meat.

They feed on unsuspecting 2._____ . For these

plants, meat is a 3._____ supplement. The

4._____ moves to catch its 5._____ ,

while the 6._____ has a sticky surface that traps its catch.

D.   Answer the questions.

1.   What have science fiction movies frightened us with?

    _____

    _____

2.   What are the types of meat-eating plants? How are they different?

    _____

    _____

    _____

    _____

3.   Describe how the Venus Flytrap attracts and preys on insects.

    _____

    _____

    _____

    _____

    _____

E. **Listen to the passage "Meat-eating Plants" again. Then write a summary in no more than 80 words.**

5.1

Include only the main points in the summary. Use your own words.

Summary

_____

_____

_____

_____

_____

_____

_____

_____

Words that I Have Learned

_____

_____

_____

_____

The "Horseless Carriage"

This passage explores the history of the modern automobile. You will learn about the ways in which Henry Ford revolutionized the production of automobiles and made them more accessible to the general public.

R1.1 Read the questions in this review before listening. Take notes as you listen. You may read the listening script on page 230 if needed.

> **Notes**

A. Circle the answers.

1. Who built the first modern automobile?

   Henry Ford

   Karl Benz

   Wilhelm Maybach

2. Mass-producing cars made them _____ .

   inefficient

   cost-effective

   costly

3. In which year did Henry Ford build his first car based on the Benz model?

   1890

   1893

   1895

4. In which year did Ford produce the Model T?

   1908

   1910

   1912

5. The more cars Henry Ford produced, the _____ .

   higher the prices were

   more expensive gas became

   lower the prices became

6. How much did the Model T cost?

   $285

   $375

   $485

7. How much did Ford pay his workers in 1914?

   $15 per month

   $5 per week

   $5 per day

8. How many cars had Ford sold by 1924?

   1.2 million

   2 million

   2.2 million

9. What did General Motors understand better than its competitors?

   marketing

   mechanics

   motors

10. People love the automobile because it gives them a sense of _____ .

    luxury and indulgence

    liability and responsibility

    freedom and excitement

B.   **Listen to the questions and answer options. Then write the correct letters in the boxes.**

R1.2

1 ☐   2 ☐   3 ☐   4 ☐

C.   **Fill in the blanks of this newspaper article with the correct words.**

THE DAILY EXPRESS

Sunday, May 24, 1913

WELCOME TO THE MODERN AGE OF FORD CARS

Henry Ford's new mode of production is revolutionary!

Henry Ford – the great innovator

The popular Ford "Model T" is a simple f_____ car without the lavish trappings of the B_____ model of cars, which the average working person cannot afford in this day and age. Now, this great a_____ is more cost-e_____ than ever.

Ford has innovated the automobile production process by introducing the first moving

a _____   l _____ and the cars are beginning to roll out!

Inspired by the continuous-flow production methods used in a s_____ he visited, Ford's assembly line significantly reduces the time it takes to build a car.

The money saved in m _____ benefits consumers everywhere, and you can now get your own Ford Model T for as little as $285!

D. **Draw lines to match the facts in the two columns.**

Column A

1. 1913

2. 1908

3. everyone

4. expensive cars

5. yearly model change

6. upper class purchasers in Europe

Column B

• Ford's target consumers

• Benz's target consumers

• built by Benz

• introduced by General Motors

• the year in which Ford's family car was introduced

• the year in which Ford created his assembly line

E. **Write "T" for the true statements and "F" for the false ones.**

1. Karl Benz was a German engineer. _____

2. Karl Benz figured out a way to mass-produce the modern automobile. _____

3. Henry Ford built his first car based on the Benz model. _____

4. Henry Ford was inspired to create an assembly line after visiting a newspaper publisher. _____

5. The assembly line is a method of production still used today. _____

6. Henry Ford introduced the yearly model change to the world of cars. _____

7. General Motors introduced the "payment plan" method of purchasing. _____

F.   **Check the innovations attributed to Henry Ford.**

1.   the creation of the first modern automobile ☐

2.   the creation of a luxury car for upper class purchasers ☐

3.   the creation of the automobile assembly line in 1913 ☐

4.   the creation of the mass production of automobiles ☐

5.   the creation of a good marketing strategy where people could purchase on credit ☐

6.   the creation of an affordable car everyone could buy ☐

G.   **Rewrite the statements so they are true.**

1.   The first modern automobile was built by General Motors.

_____

2.   In 1913, Ford created the Model T, a family car with the fancy trappings found on expensive cars.

_____

_____

3.   The more cars Henry Ford produced, the higher the prices grew.

_____

4.   By 1924, Ford had sold more than 2.5 million cars.

_____

5.   Ford managed to get the price of the Model T down to $485.

_____

_____

H. Answer the questions.

1. Explain the innovations General Motors introduced to the automobile industry.

_____

_____

_____

2. Why did some professionals think that Ford would go bankrupt?

_____

_____

_____

I. **Listen to the passage "The Horseless Carriage" again. Then write a summary in no more than 80 words.**

Listen carefully to make sure you catch all of the important points of the passage to include them in your summary. Use your own words.

_____

_____

_____

_____

_____

_____

_____

_____

Grammar

UNIT

1 Nouns

A **noun** names a person, an animal, a place, or a thing. Nouns can be classified as **countable common nouns**, **uncountable common nouns**, and **proper nouns**.

Examples

Common Noun		Proper Noun
Countable	Uncountable	
house	rice	Montreal
coat	air	Michael

A. Read the story and write the nouns in the table.

Today my sister and I arrived in Dublin. Our aunt and cousin came to meet us at the airport. Tomorrow we will travel to Cork City, and next week, we will tour the Ring of Kerry. Ireland is beautiful; the scenery is breathtaking. For the third week of our vacation, we have planned to go to London to visit more relatives. We are going to have a fun time exploring the city. Maybe we will even get to visit Buckingham Palace! I cannot wait for all the excitement that lies ahead!

Common Noun		Proper Noun
Countable	Uncountable	

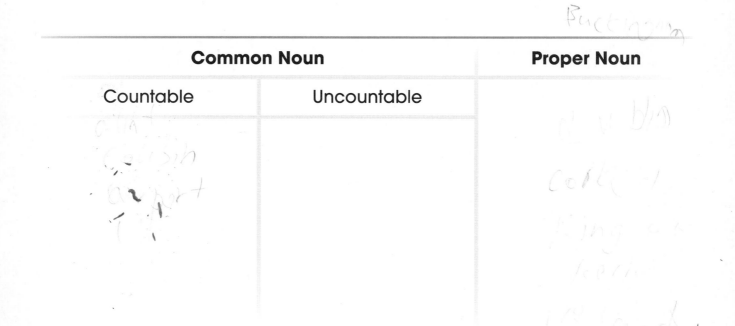

Collective nouns are used to refer to groups of people, animals, and things.

A collective noun is a countable noun and can be singular or plural, depending on the context.

Examples

- a <u>litter</u> of kittens
  singular

- two <u>bouquets</u> of
  plural
  flowers

B. Fill in the blanks with the correct collective nouns.

1. I ate a _____ of grapes yesterday.

2. We played with a _____ of cards.

3. The _____ of cows is in the meadow.

4. The _____ of bees buzzes in the garden.

5. The best _____ of players in the country is the Blue Giants!

| deck |
| bunch |
| swarm |
| team |
| herd |

C. Check to indicate whether the underlined collective nouns are singular or plural.

	singular	plural
1. The <u>class</u> is rehearsing for the school concert.	◯	◯
2. The <u>gaggle</u> of geese is flying south.	◯	◯
3. My <u>family</u> have dinner at different times.	◯	◯
4. The <u>gang</u> of robbers left their personal items behind.	◯	✓
5. The <u>school</u> of salmon was moving upstream.	◯	◯
6. The <u>association</u> enforces strict policies on its members.	◯	◯
7. The <u>panel</u> of judges were making their own decisions.	◯	◯
8. The <u>band</u> of musicians played harmoniously.	✓	◯

Abstract nouns refer to intangible things like feelings, ideas, qualities, and states. A noun is abstract if you cannot hear, see, touch, smell, or taste it. It is uncountable.

Examples

- Feeling: love
- Idea: faith
- Quality: beauty
- State: prosperity

D. Read the story. Underline the abstract nouns. Then sort and write them in the correct boxes.

The Haunted Castle

Melinda had been suffering from a minor illness. As her health improved, her mother saw it as an opportunity to fulfill her dream of visiting a haunted castle.

Full of excitement and fear, they arrived at the castle. Melinda held onto her favourite necklace for luck as she stepped inside. She was able to rely on her bravery and confidence as she made her way through a web of scary spiders and spooky ghosts! Finally, she realized that she could overcome anything if she remained calm and determined.

Abstract Nouns

Feeling	Idea	Quality	State

E. **Look at the pictures and write sentences with the correct nouns.**

Collective Noun			Abstract Noun	
pack	bunch	flock	love	peace

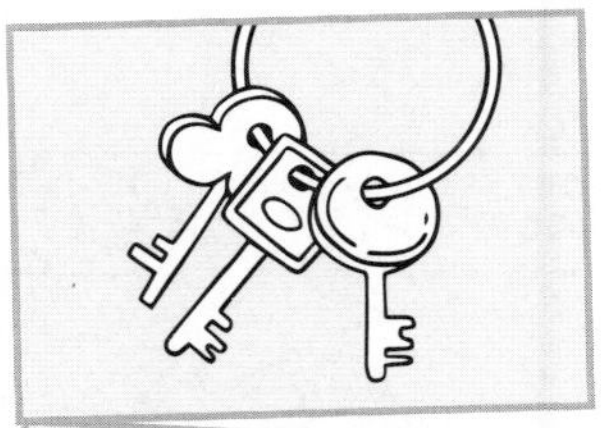

_____

_____

_____

_____

_____

_____

_____

_____

Words that I Have Learned

Nouns

_____

_____

_____

UNIT

2 Direct and Indirect Objects

A noun can be the object of a verb in a sentence.

A **direct object** is the receiver of the action of a verb.

Example

Casey mailed the <u>package</u>.
direct object

A. Underline the verbs and circle the direct objects in the sentences.

1. The pianist played a wonderful song at the beginning of the event.

2. Lucy ate the entire cake in the kitchen after school.

3. Carly wore a pretty dress to the party last night.

4. Andy ordered some gifts from an online company.

5. Emma's dog catches the Frisbee with his big mouth.

6. The farmer ploughed his fields in the morning.

7. The guest speaker is giving a speech on the ancient Egyptian civilization.

8. Samuel bought some drinks for the birthday party.

9. The teacher opened the windows to let in some fresh air.

10. Dad parked his car in the driveway last night.

11. The choir sang melodious songs in the concert.

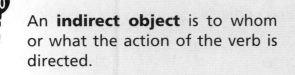

An **indirect object** is to whom or what the action of the verb is directed.

Casey mailed <u>Walter</u> the package.
indirect object

B. **Read each sentence. Then check the circle if the underlined word is an indirect object. Put a cross if it is not.**

1. Jason built his <u>daughter</u> a sandcastle. ✓

2. Janice lent Wendy her new <u>scooter</u>. ✗

3. The sweet music is playing in the <u>lounge</u>. ◯

4. Bobby sends his <u>buddy</u> a postcard from Paris. ◯

5. Sean showed <u>Kathy</u> an interesting picture. ◯

6. Jonathan gave his story a <u>title</u>. ◯

7. Bert and his family live a few <u>blocks</u> away. ◯

8. I handed the <u>keys</u> to my uncle before I left. ◯

9. Tammy gave her <u>dog</u> delicious treats from time to time. ◯

10. We made our mom a <u>card</u> for Mother's Day. ◯

11. Grandma told me her secret <u>recipe</u> for the pot pie. ◯

12. Why don't you write <u>me</u> a letter? ◯

Section
2

Grammar

C. **Read the sentences. Then circle to indicate whether the underlined words are direct objects or indirect objects.**

Object

1. The players wore <u>sweaters</u> for the game.　　　　direct / indirect

2. People who live in the forest cut <u>trees</u> for shelters.　　direct / indirect

3. The mother told her <u>daughter</u> stories about her youth.　direct / indirect

4. He gave <u>her</u> a ride to school yesterday.　　　　　direct / indirect

5. He asked the <u>person</u> in front of him to move over.　direct / indirect

6. They gave the charity a lot of <u>money</u>.　　　　　direct / indirect

7. The father read his <u>son</u> a bedtime story.　　　　direct / indirect

8. The library showed the <u>children</u> films on Saturday.　direct / indirect

D. **Fill in the boxes with the correct words. Then colour the boxes.**

| bicycle | drink |
| himself | top |

direct object green

indirect object red

Michael rode his [　　] up the hill. When he reached the

[　　　　] , he was tired, so he gave

[　　　] a break. He took a [　　　]

from his water bottle and put it back in his backpack.

E. Write "D" in the circles if the underlined words are direct objects. Write "I" if they are indirect objects.

It was a dark and stormy night. Emily had just finished reading her <u>book</u> ◯

and wanted to get <u>herself</u> (I) a <u>snack</u> ◯ from the kitchen. Other than

her cat and the occasional field mouse, the house was empty. Only the

sound of leaves rustling outside could be heard. When Emily reached the

<u>bottom of the staircase</u> ◯ , she saw a <u>mouse</u> ◯ scurrying around the

corner. Normally, this would not have given <u>her</u> ◯ the <u>creeps</u> ◯ , but

on this particular night, Emily had an eerie <u>feeling</u> ◯ that the mouse was

trying to tell <u>her</u> ◯ <u>something</u> ◯ . It stared

at her and she did not know how to react.

Then suddenly, she felt a <u>wisp of air</u> ◯ over

her head. Emily turned around to see what

had brought <u>home</u> ◯ the <u>wind</u> ◯ . It was

her cat. It had leapt from the staircase railing, wearing the <u>cape</u> ◯ that

Emily had put on it earlier. The mouse gave <u>the cat</u> ◯ a startled <u>look</u> ◯

and scurried away.

Words that I Have Learned

_____

_____

_____

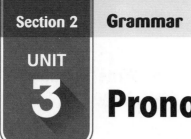

UNIT

3 Pronouns

A **subject pronoun** takes the place of the subject noun in a sentence and an **object pronoun** takes the place of the object noun.

Example

subject noun ┌object noun

Susan likes apples. She likes them
                    subject pronoun   object pronoun

because they are sweet.
         subject pronoun

A. Circle the correct subject pronouns in blue and the correct object pronouns in red to complete the sentences.

1. Archie missed school yesterday because **he** / **it** was sick.

2. **I** / **You** am going to bake a huge cake tomorrow.

3. The children danced with **him** / **we** at the party.

4. My mother is a teacher. **They** / **She** teaches Drama and Music.

5. **Us** / **We** saw Kate at the park yesterday but **her** / **she** did not see **us** / **we** .

6. "**Them** / **They** can go to the movies with **me** / **I** ," said Mom.

7. Susie watched the whole movie because **we** / **she** enjoyed **it** / **them** .

8. **I** / **She** am going to eat at the Italian restaurant with **he** / **him** .

9. **He** / **They** kicked the ball over the hedge and went to get **you** / **it** back.

B. **Fill in the blanks with the correct pronouns. Then write "S" in the boxes if they are subject pronouns. Write "O" if they are object pronouns.**

1. There is a squirrel in the backyard.

   ___it___ [S] is burying its food in

   the ground.

2. It was Jerry's birthday yesterday. His

   friend took ___him___ [O] out for dinner.

3. Flora was bored so her father gave ___her___ [O] an interesting book

   to read.

4. Mr. Brown was off from work yesterday. ___he___ [S] took his children

   to a water park. ___They___ [S] had fun there.

5. Jenny asked Carol, "Do you want to meet Betty and ___me___ [O]

   at the restaurant? We can have dinner there together."

6. Little Kate is very tired. ___She___ [S] has already gone to bed.

7. Bruce is scared of the thunderstorm.

   ___It___ [S] is loud and alarming.

8. "Mom and Dad, ___I___ [S] have

   won the race!" Fred said as he proudly

   showed ___them___ [O] his gold medal.

A **reflexive pronoun** is a type of object pronoun. We use it when the subject's action turns back on the subject.

Example

The cat cleans <u>itself</u> with its tongue.

C.   Underline the reflexive pronoun in each sentence. Check the circle if it is correct. If not, put a cross and write the correct reflexive pronoun above it.

1.   Danny made himself a big, yummy breakfast.   ✓

2.   Maggie taught itself how to skate.   ◯

3.   I wash ourselves when I get up in the morning.   ◯

4.   "Did you make this card himself?" Mrs. Robin asked her son.   ◯

5.   The little mice hid itself behind the piano when they saw the cat.   ◯

6.   Emma set herself an impossible task at the beginning of the year.   ✓

7.   After we fell, we picked yourself up with Ms. Hall's encouragement.   ◯

8.   The bird built itself a nest in the tree early this morning.   ✓

9.   "Don't get myself into trouble again!" Mr. Morris reminded us.   ◯

10.   My sister and I had to look after herself last night because Mom and Dad were not home.   ◯

11.   Gina and Dennis treated themselves to ice cream sundaes after a long day of hard work.   ✓

D. **Rewrite the sentences using pronouns for the underlined words.**

1. <u>Kathy</u> told <u>Mr. Evans</u> her name.

   _____

2. <u>Ryan</u> ate <u>the cookies</u> in the kitchen.

   _____

3. <u>The students</u> found <u>the kitten</u> yesterday.

   _____

4. <u>Larry and I</u> will meet <u>Alice</u> at the entrance.

   _____

E. **Write sentences of your own with the reflexive pronouns.**

myself	I made myself a toy
itself	the cat washed itself
themselves	They made themselves a book
ourselves	we hid ourselves in a tree

Words that I Have Learned

Pronouns

_____

_____

_____

Modal Verbs

The **modal verb** "can" is used to talk about ability in the present or future. It is also used to give or ask permission in the present or future.

Examples

- ability
  Pat <u>can</u> play the piano but Lucy <u>cannot</u>.

- permission
  "<u>Can</u> we have a snack before bed?" asked the children.

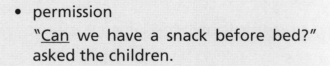

A. **Circle the modal verbs in the sentences. Then write the letters to indicate whether the modal verbs are used to talk about ability or to give or ask permission.**

A Beavers can build amazing dams.

B "You're kidding me, Richard!" says Tom. "Beavers can't sing!"

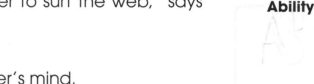

C "Sure, you can use my computer to surf the web," says Michael to Todd.

Ability

D Sydney's dog can read his owner's mind.

E Bob cannot go to the baseball game tonight because he is grounded for a week.

F Fran is only five but she can already swim quite well.

Permission

G "No, you cannot eat all the cookies in the jar," says Mother.

H You can drive to Germany from France but you cannot do that from Australia.

I "Can I invite three more friends to the party?" asked Karen.

Examples

We use "**could**" to talk about ability or permission in the past. We also use "could" to talk about possibility.

- ability
  Leila <u>could</u> talk when she was barely two.

- permission
  Mom said I <u>could</u> go hiking with you.

- possibility
  It <u>could</u> start raining any minute.

B. **Circle the modal verbs in the sentences. Then write "A" for ability, "P" for permission, and "PO" for possibility.**

1. "The bell could ring any second now," says Mr. Graham. _____

2. Grandpa could read four newspapers in one afternoon back in the days when he was young. _____

3. Jeremiah asked his parents if he could have the last piece of pumpkin pie. _____

4. Melissa said I could borrow her books when she finished reading them. _____

5. The line-up was so crowded yesterday that nobody could move an inch. _____

6. Christine could juggle three balls when she worked at the circus last summer. _____

7. Larry's parents told him that he could sleep over at my place this weekend. _____

8.  There could be a thunderstorm tomorrow. _____

Examples

We use "**will**", "**would**", and "**could**" to ask for assistance in a polite way.

- <u>Will</u> you please buy some eggs?

- <u>Would</u> you please deliver this box?

- <u>Could</u> you open the door for me?

C. Fill in the blanks with "will", "would", or "could".

1. There's no more milk in the fridge. _____ you pick up a few cartons from the grocery store?

   Sure, I will.

2. The phone is ringing but my hands are full. _____ you please answer the phone for me?

   Yes, of course.

3. It's getting hot in the classroom. _____ you open the window?

   Sure, no problem.

4. I'm trying to study. _____ you turn the stereo down a bit?

   Sure!

D. Ask a polite question with "will", "would", or "could" for each picture.

"**Could**" is more polite than "**can**" because "could" suggests possibility while "can" is more definite. By using "could" to ask for assistance, we give the other person more room to think about our request.

A. _____

B. _____

C. _____

Words that I Have Learned

Modal Verbs

_____

_____

_____

5 Simple and Progressive Tenses

We use the **simple present tense** when talking about a habit or a simple truth.

We use the **present progressive tense** when talking about an action that is going on, or an action that will take place in the near future.

Examples

- Jim <u>drinks</u> a glass of milk every morning.
- Ava <u>is wrapping</u> presents for her friends.
- Liam <u>is coming</u> tomorrow.

A. Underline the verbs in the wrong tenses in the sentences. Then correct them by changing the simple present tense verbs to the present progressive tense and vice versa. Write above the underlined verbs.

1. Look! The children run toward the ice cream truck.

2. Bernie is singing a pretty song every morning.

3. Nicky shows Jack her new running shoes now.

4. Listen! The breeze blows through the trees in the forest.

5. Shelby is looking after her baby sister whenever her mother is out.

6. "I can't talk to you now. I drive," Dad said.

7. Mrs. Watt is reading her son a bedtime story every night.

8. Bobby is giving his dog a bath once every three weeks.

We use the **simple past tense** when talking about something that happened habitually or at a particular time in the past.

We use the **past progressive tense** when talking about something that continued to happen over a period of time.

Examples

- Cindy <u>woke</u> up early yesterday.
- Aydin <u>was watching</u> TV when the doorbell rang.

B. Circle the verbs in the correct tenses to complete the sentences.

1. Benjamin **flew / was flying** happily in his dream when his little sister woke him up.

2. Cassandra's friends often **talked / were talking** to her while she was studying.

3. Martin **walked / was walking** to the library when he bumped into an old friend from kindergarten.

4. Margaret **rehearsed / was rehearsing** with the choir when she was called to the office.

5. Wayne often **played / was playing** catch with his buddies last summer.

6. The telephone rang when I **took / was taking** a shower.

7. Jade **ate / was eating** dinner when someone knocked on her front door.

8. Keith was debating whether to get a banana split or a strawberry sundae when he **spotted / was spotting** a chocolate fudge sandwich on the menu and **decided / was deciding** to order that instead.

We use the **simple future tense** when talking about something that will happen.

We use the **future progressive tense** when talking about something that will happen over a period of time.

Examples

- It <u>will be</u> warm and sunny tomorrow.
- Richard <u>will be napping</u> for the rest of the day.

C. **Rewrite the sentences with the underlined verbs in the correct simple future tense or future progressive tense.**

1. Many of us <u>watch</u> the parade on TV.

   _____

2. The phone <u>ring</u> in five minutes.

   _____

3. Vinnie's cousin <u>visit</u> for the summer.

   _____

4. There <u>be</u> a new radio program on Monday morning.

   _____

5. Marty <u>attend</u> a different school for some time.

   _____

6. Karl's children <u>play</u> one more game before they have to leave.

   _____

   _____

7. Since it is so hot, they <u>swim</u> until sunset.

   _____

   _____

D. **Write sentences using the given words in the specified tenses.**

1. boy   eat   egg   every   day   (simple present)

     _____

2. farmers   milk   cows   now   (present progressive)

     _____

3. teachers   have   meeting   yesterday   (simple past)

     _____

4. they   play   soccer   all   day   (past progressive)

     _____

5. Stephanie   Aiden   buy   cookbook   mother   tomorrow
    (simple future)

     _____

     _____

6. Sam   mow   lawn   entire   afternoon
    Saturday   (future progressive)

     _____

     _____

Words that I Have Learned

_____

_____

_____

UNIT

6 Perfect Tenses

have to

The **present perfect tense** can be used to show:

- an action completed at an unspecified time before the present

- an action started in the past that continues up to the present

- an action completed in the past that affects the present

It is formed with "has/have" followed by the past participle of a verb.

Examples

- I have skied before.
- The Lees have lived in that mansion for years.
- Sally has torn the page by accident.

tear
tore

A. Check if the sentences are in the present perfect tense.

1. Tim has been a lawyer for almost ten years. ☑

2. The plants have grown under good conditions. ☐

3. Jeffrey went hiking in the mountains. ☐

4. Mr. Hart's house has a beautiful garden. ☐

5. Why are you counting the books? ☐

6. I have had horrible nightmares lately. ☐

7. The children have finished their dinner quickly. ☑

8. There has been a traffic jam since noon. ☑

9. Grandpa has read a lot of books this summer. ☑

10. Mom and Dad took us out for dinner last night. ☐

11. Laura has made eight bracelets for her friends. ☑

The **past perfect tense** shows an action that took place before another event in the past (with the verb in the simple past tense). It is formed with "had" followed by the past participle of a verb.

Example

She <u>had met</u> him before I introduced them.

B. Fill in the blanks with the verbs in the past perfect tense.

1. He _____ (study) English before his family came to Canada.

2. Danny _____ (finish) breakfast when I left for work.

3. My mother _____ (go) upstairs when we walked into the living room.

4. The plane _____ (land) when I arrived at the airport.

5. Terrence _____ (take) off his shoes before he entered the house.

6. After Sasha _____ (clean) the shelf, she put the books back on it.

7. Jamie's sister _____ (eat) all the cookies by the time he got home.

8. Kurt _____ (knock) on the door before he entered the office.

9. The boys _____ (play) soccer before they joined the team.

10. The team won the game after they _____ (practise) for months.

C.   Underline the verbs that show the perfect tenses in the sentences. Then fill in the blanks with the given words.

Words Used with the Perfect Tenses

ever	never	since	before	already
yet	so far	recently	just	for after

1.   Janet has decided _____recently_____ to move to Canada.

2.   She had waited for her friends for 20 minutes ____before____ they arrived.

3.   My father has worked as an engineer ____for____ ten years.

4.   Mrs. Price had not ____yet____ finished playing the movie when the doorbell rang.

5.   The concert had ____just____ started to get louder!

6.   They have _____ played hockey together.

7.   Quinn has played the violin ____since____ she was eight.

8.   Have you ____ever____ been to a haunted castle?

9.   Dad has only painted two bedrooms ____so far____.

10.   Rick began to get up earlier only _____ he had started school again.

11.   Ali and Alya had ____already____ begun rehearsing the play when the other cast members arrived.

D. **Write sentences in the perfect tenses with the given words.**

Present Perfect Tense

1. dance

   never

2. take

   since

3. collect

   for

Past Perfect Tense

1. try   ever

   before

2. know   yet

   when

3. write   already

   before

Words that I Have Learned

UNIT 7 Active and Passive Voice

Examples

We use the **active voice** when we want to talk about a person or thing doing something.

We use the **passive voice** when we want to focus on the person or thing affected by an action.

- Active Voice

  Mom baked a cake yesterday.

- Passive Voice

  A cake was baked yesterday.

A. Match to show the voice of the sentences.

Jason played with his dog in the backyard.

The dishes were washed after the table was cleaned.

Dinner was served later than expected.

Jane bought a new purse while she was in Montreal.

Hannah walked over to Dominic's house.

The director explained the script to the actors.

The letter was delivered to the secret agent.

Active Voice

Passive Voice

B. Write the sentence numbers in the correct boxes.

1 Rebecca was driven to school by her father.

2 The teacher gave the students more time to work on their assignments.

3 This lock has never been opened.

4 All the toys on the table were made by elves.

5 Alice carried the magic potion carefully upstairs.

6 Snacks will be served before the lecture.

7 Ted wished on the shooting star.

8 The mouse was chased by the cat.

9 The fisherman cast the net into the sea.

10 The happy child opened all his birthday gifts after the party.

11 Denise found her lost lucky charm in the corner.

12 The participants were rewarded for their hard work.

Active Voice	Passive Voice

C.   **Fill in the blanks with the verbs in the passive voice in the past tense.**

> The passive voice is formed with the correct form of "be" followed by the past participle of a verb.

e.g. It was eaten...

1.   The bag _____ (put) in the overhead compartment.

2.   The passengers _____ (tell) there would be a delay.

3.   Carmen _____ (give) some paper and crayons.

4.   A cute airplane _____ (draw) by Carmen.

5.   Clouds could _____ (see) through the windows.

6.   The passengers were happy that they _____ (provide) with the weather report.

7.   Desserts and drinks _____ (offer) to the passengers.

8.   Carmen _____ (serve) a meal of pasta and meatballs.

9.   Travel pillows _____ (lend) to eveyone on board.

10.   Some extra napkins _____ (hand) to Carmen.

D. **Rewrite each sentence in the passive voice without mentioning the doer of the action.**

> When using the passive voice, the person or thing that performs the action is not always mentioned.

1. Mom watered the flowers yesterday.

   _____

2. The thief stole the invaluable antiques.

   _____

3. Sandra repeated the whole story to the detectives.

   _____

4. The wind blew Natalie's scarf away.

   _____

5. The kind man donated many toys to the charity group.

   _____

6. The author wrote this book in 2015.

   _____

Words that I Have Learned

_____

_____

_____

UNIT 8 Direct and Indirect Speech

Direct speech shows the exact words a speaker used. Direct speech is placed within quotation marks.

Example
The boy cried, "Help! There's a wolf near the sheep!"

A. Add quotation marks where appropriate to the sentences in direct speech.

1. Wait! I don't want to be late for school! Liz cried as she ran after the bus.

2. Everybody deserves a second chance! the kind lady said.

3. Call me again tomorrow, said Mom.

4. The elves cheered, Long live King Julian!

5. Jason, do you want butter or jam? asked Mrs. Brown.

6. The teacher instructed, Write your name on the first page of the book.

7. Trisha said, Fish soup is my favourite on a cold winter day.

8. The coffee is not hot enough! the customer complained.

9. You can find the information on the website, Karen answered.

10. I heard some noises from the kitchen, Daniel whispered.

11. Let's go jogging in the park tomorrow morning, Dad suggested.

12. Little Kate asked curiously, Can your puppy swim?

Direct speech is accompanied by an **introductory clause**, which identifies the speaker and sometimes the listener. Use a comma after the introductory clause when it comes before the quoted words; use a period when it comes after them.

Examples

- speaker

  • <u>Zoe</u> said , "I like pears."

  introductory clause

- listener

  • "I like pears," Zoe told <u>Ian</u>.

  introductory clause

B. **Underline the introductory clause in each sentence. Then circle the reporting verb.**

> *An introductory clause contains a **reporting verb**, which is usually in the simple past tense.*

Reporting Verb

1. "Is your friend going with you?" asked Mom.

2. "Cats have nine lives," Quincy whispered to Nora.

3. "The thieves took everything!" mourned the woman.

4. Sharon told her dad, "I made a new friend today!"

5. "Watch out! Don't step on my truck!" Alan's brother screamed.

6. Larry confessed, "I've broken your favourite mug, Mom."

7. "I don't like pineapple on pizza," Jay complained to his friend.

8. The suspect replied, "I wasn't in town when the burglary took place."

9. "Let's go to the cottage this weekend," Pansy suggested.

10. Peter says, "Your ice cream cone looks really good."

Examples

The quoted words enclosed in quotation marks in direct speech end in a comma, a question mark, or an exclamation mark. If the direct speech is at the end of the sentence, it can end in a period.

- "I'm full**,**" Jen said.

- "Do you want my cheesecake**?**" she asked Carl.

- "I'm full, too. I can't eat any more**!**" Carl replied.

C. **Add the correct punctuation marks in the circles.**

1. "Grandpa, are you visiting us this weekend ◯ " Sasha asked.

2. "I'm going to buy some drinks for the party ◯ " said Mr. Hall.

3. "That's totally unacceptable ◯ " the customer complained.

4. "How many days are there in a year ◯ " Toby asked.

5. His mom answered, "There are 365 days in a year ◯ "

6. "We really can't stay any longer ◯ " George insisted.

7. The teacher reminded the students, "Remember to hand in your project tomorrow ◯ "

8. Dr. Perry advised me, "You should eat more vegetables ◯ "

9. The children asked, "Could we play for another hour ◯ "

10. Levi exclaimed, "This is the most amazing magic show I've seen ◯ "

11. "Isn't this the song you mentioned yesterday ◯ " asked Ana.

12. "The capital city of Alberta is Edmonton ◯ " Jerry answered.

Indirect speech reports what someone said. No quotation marks are needed.

Changing direct speech to indirect speech involves changes in tense. The tense in indirect speech is one tense back in time from that in direct speech.

Examples

- Direct Speech:

"I <u>want</u> tea," Mom said.
present tense

- Indirect Speech:

Mom said that she <u>wanted</u> tea.
past tense

D. **Fill in the blanks with the verbs in the correct forms to change the direct speech to indirect speech.**

1. "I like reading," Marie said.

   Marie said that she _____ reading.

2. "The curry is too spicy!" Jeromy complained.

   _____ that the

   curry _____ too spicy.

3. "I do not know the answer," Janet admitted.

   Janet admitted that _____ .

4. "We need a break," the children said.

   _____

Words that I Have Learned

_____

_____

_____

UNIT

9 Adjectives

Tim
Sam
Sue

We use **comparative adjectives** to compare two people, animals, things, or groups. We use **superlative adjectives** when the comparison is among three or more.

Examples

- Comparative
  Sue is <u>taller</u> than Sam.

- Superlative
  Tim is the <u>tallest</u> among the children.

A.   Complete the table by writing the comparative and superlative forms of each adjective.

	Adjective	Comparative	Superlative
1.	safe		
2.	tiny		tiniest
3.	sad	sadder	
4.	great		
5.	friendly		
6.	forgetful	more forgetful	
7.	influential		most influential
8.	big		
9.	happy		
10.	nice		
11.	lively		
12.	 thin		

B. Rewrite the sentences with the correct comparative or superlative adjectives.

1. Marie's room is the most tidy in the house.

    _____

2. We had the splendidest dinner in Little Italy.

    _____

3. Kim's mother makes the most smooth cheesecake I have ever had.

    _____

4. This restaurant is popularer than the one beside it.

    _____

5. Marcus is usually more fast than Gilbert.

    _____

6. Canada is the beautifulest country in the world!

    _____

7. Judy is the most tall girl in her class.

    _____

8. Bella was carefuller than her cousin Robin.

    _____

9. This light is a bit more dim than the others.

    _____

10.

    I think soccer is excitinger than hockey!

    _____

    _____

Many verbs can become adjectives when we add "ing" or "ed" to them. In general, "-ing" adjectives describe the effect of someone or something while "-ed" adjectives describe someone's feelings.

Examples

- Lori's skipping ability is <u>amazing</u>. (effect)

- Lori's friends are <u>amazed</u>. (feeling)

C.   Form adjectives with the correct forms of the verbs and fill in the blanks.

1.   Clara was _____ (scare) when she saw the bat.

2.   The film was so _____ (move) that I wept while watching it.

3.   We strolled along the _____ (charm) street at sunset.

4.   Looking at the calm sea is _____ (relax).

5.   My friends and I were _____ (surprise) to find an old _____ (lock) chest in the attic.

6.   The guest speaker's speech at the conference yesterday was really _____ (encourage).

7.   She turned her _____ (rip) jeans into a beautiful purse.

8.   Desmond was so _____ (worry) that he stayed wide awake all night.

9.   The _____ (deafen) thunder woke everyone up in the middle of the night.

10. The decrease in the number of many animal species is _____ (alarm).

11. The students were _____ (excite) to pick strawberries on their school outing.

D. **Create two adjectives with each verb. Then fill in the blanks and write sentences with them.**

	A confuse	**B** bore	**C** interest	**D** tire
-ing	_____	_____	_____	_____
-ed	_____	_____	_____	_____

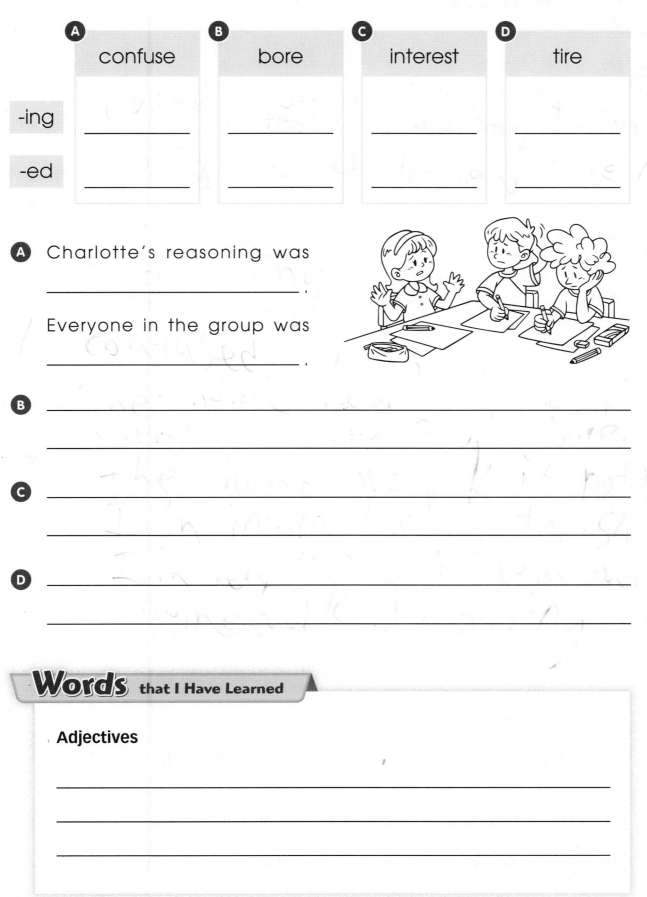

A Charlotte's reasoning was
_____ .
Everyone in the group was
_____ .

B _____

_____

C _____

_____

D _____

_____

Words that I Have Learned

Adjectives

_____

_____

_____

UNIT

10   **Adverbs**

Comparative and **superlative adverbs** are formed and used in the same way as comparative and superlative adjectives.

Examples

- Mia arrived <u>earlier</u> than her friend.
- The smallest puppy barked <u>loudest</u> of all the puppies in the litter.

A.   Write the comparative and superlative forms of each adverb.

Adverb	Comparative	Superlative
1. cautiously		
2. early		
3. badly		
4. far		
5. quickly		
6. often		
7. well		

B.   Circle the correct forms of the adverbs to complete the sentences.

1. Andy swam **faster / fastest** and won the championship.

2. I climbed **higher / highest** than you!

3. Julian spoke **more convincingly / most convincingly** among all the participants.

4. We went to class **earlier / earliest** today than yesterday.

5. The tortoise ran **slower / slowest** than the hare.

C.   Fill in the blanks with the correct forms of the adverbs to complete the sentences.

1. Terry has been visiting his grandpa

    _____ (frequently)

    over the past two weeks.

2. The _____ (late)

    we arrive, the less time we will have

    to explore the city.

3. The _____ (soon) Marla gets better, the faster she can

    resume training.

4. Sam is like a bird. Of everyone in his family, he always gets up

    _____ (early).

5. Sometimes he will get a coffee or a hot chocolate, but he orders tea

    _____ (often).

6. The youngest performer stood _____ (confidently) in

    front of the audience.

7. Aria writes _____ (fast) and _____

    (neatly) than her sister.

8. Everette sat _____ (close) to the exit than anyone else

    because he had to leave early.

9. This bus goes _____ (far) north than that one.

10. Gianna's voice could be heard _____ (clearly) in the

    group.

D.   **Check if the adverbs are in the correct forms. Underline the wrong adverb forms and write the correct forms above them.**

1.   The postcard arrived sooner than Nova had expected.   ◯

2.   The fairy walked most lightly than the elf.   ◯

3.   She dealt with emergencies calmer than Yan.   ◯

4.   The dog ran farthest into the forest than the cat.   ◯

5.   He kicked the ball most powerfully among all members on the team.   ◯

6.   Of all the children, Jayce spoke softer.   ◯

7.   After failing the test, Sophie worked hardest than before.   ◯

8.   That frog jumps most highly even though it is the smallest one over there.   ◯

9.   I sing worse in my family but I like singing.   ◯

10.   Miles worked on the project more happily than Vincent.   ◯

11.   Alana danced most gracefully than the other ballerinas.   ◯

12.   Claudia cried hardest among her classmates at the end of the sad movie.   ◯

E. Write the comparative and superlative forms of each adverb. Then complete the sentence or write a sentence with the words.

1.

brightly
_____
_____

That star shines _____ than the other stars but the moon shines _____ in the night sky.

2.

near
_____
_____

_____

_____

_____

3.

carefully
_____
_____

_____

_____

_____

4.

late
_____
_____

_____

_____

_____

Words that I Have Learned

Adverbs

_____

_____

_____

UNIT

11 Phrases

A **phrase** is a group of two or more words that forms a single part of speech in a sentence.

A **noun phrase** functions like a noun in a sentence. It can be the subject, object, or the complement*. It can simply be one or more nouns, or a combination of nouns and other words, like adjectives.

*A complement is a noun phrase that follows a form of the verb "be".

Example

<u>Little Ashley</u> is
subject

building <u>a big snowman,</u>
object

which is <u>her first snowman</u>
complement

this winter.

A. **Identify the underlined noun phrases as subjects, objects, or complements. Write "subject", "object", or "complement" on the lines.**

1. <u>Lindsay and her mom</u> have just gone into a new grocery store.

   _____

2. The things they need to buy are <u>bread, some deli meats, snacks, and detergent</u>.

   _____

3. Lindsay wants to get <u>a pack of salad mix</u> for lunch.

   _____

4. Lindsay also wants some chocolate ice cream because it is <u>her favourite ice cream</u>.

   _____

5. Lindsay's mom tells Lindsay that in the fridge at home are <u>some chopped up cauliflower sticks</u>.

   _____

6. Lindsay returns <u>the shopping cart</u> to the front of the store.

   _____

7. <u>The two of them</u> went home happily with the bags of groceries.

   _____

An **adjective phrase** functions like an adjective in a sentence. It describes a noun.

An **adverb phrase** functions like an adverb in a sentence. It describes a verb.

Examples

- Adjective Phrase

  Megan has a <u>very big</u> smile on her face.

- Adverb Phrase

  Megan's brother thinks his sister is <u>too easily</u> pleased.

B. **Identify the words in bold in the sentences as adjective phrases or adverb phrases. Check the circles.**

		Adjective Phrase	Adverb Phrase
1.	Jason can build **tall and impressive** towers with cards.	◯	◯
2.	He can build them **so quickly** that he amazes his friends.	◯	◯
3.	He can finish building a tower **quite comfortably** in five minutes.	◯	◯
4.	He was not **that skilful** in building towers with cards at first.	◯	◯
5.	Sometimes, Jason gets up **unusually early** to practise his hobby.	◯	◯
6.	Jason's towers are **incredibly sturdy**.	◯	◯
7.	He always puts down each card **very carefully**.	◯	◯
8.	Jason thinks his hobby is **fun and interesting**.	◯	◯

An **infinitive phrase** contains a verb that follows "to".

Example

Little Ben crawls toward his sister <u>to hold her hand</u>.

C. **Complete the sentences with the correct infinitive phrases.**

- to ride on the carousel
- to ride on the roller-coaster
- to sit down on
- to get some food
- to go to the amusement park
- to share some fries with Kim and Rachel

1. Rachel and her cousins woke up early this Saturday morning _____ _____.

2. Both Rachel and her younger cousin Kim are tall enough _____ _____.

3. Since Kim loves horses, Rachel went with her _____ _____.

4. After riding on the carousel, Kim and Rachel found a bench _____ _____.

5. Rachel's other cousins, Liz and Michelle, were hungry so they ran off _____.

6. Before long, they came back _____ _____.

A **gerund phrase** contains a verb in the "-ing" form. It can function as the subject, object, complement, or the object of a preposition in a sentence.

Examples

- <u>Playing softball</u> is fun.
  subject

- Jim likes <u>playing softball</u>.
  object

- The greatest fun is <u>playing softball</u>.
  complement

D. Identify each underlined gerund phrase as a subject (S), an object (O), a complement (C), or an object of a preposition (P).

> *I am good at <u>playing softball</u>.*
> object of a preposition

1. Maria is not very good at <u>preparing meals</u>. (   )

2. Jack enjoys <u>playing street hockey with his neighbours</u>. (   )

3. <u>Reading storybooks</u> is one of the best things to do in your spare time. (   )

4. Amanda's favourite activity is <u>spending long holidays at the family cottage</u>. (   )

5. <u>Forgiving your siblings for their mistakes</u> is not hard to do. (   )

Section 2
Grammar

Words that I Have Learned

_____

_____

_____

UNIT 12 Clauses

An **independent clause** can function as a complete sentence.

A **dependent clause** cannot function as a complete sentence. It needs an independent clause to make its meaning complete.

Example

Though the monster disappeared,
dependent

the children kept screaming.
independent

A. Colour the boxes with independent clauses yellow and those with dependent clauses green.

1. When the weather is nice outside , Gabriel likes to climb trees.

2. The children all went out to play because it was a sunny day .

3. When spring arrives , Marie will plant lots of flowers.

4. When are you arriving ?

5. Before you leave, remember to pack a sweater in your suitcase .

6. You can mail the card before you go to the library.

7. How much are these nectarines ?

8. If we go there early in the morning , we can avoid the crowds.

9. Zadie likes riding her bicycle .

B. **Identify the clauses as independent or dependent. Then match the clauses to form sentences.**

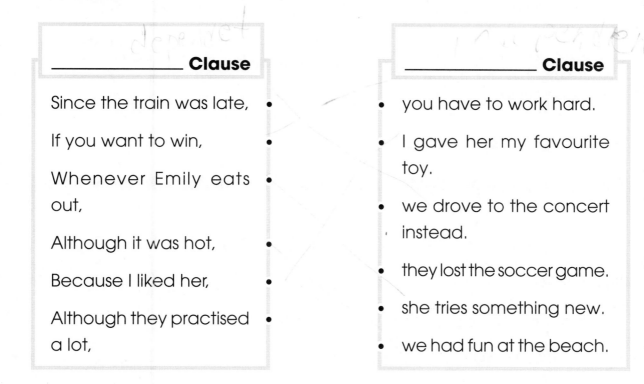

dependent **Clause**

Since the train was late, •

If you want to win, •

Whenever Emily eats out, •

Although it was hot, •

Because I liked her, •

Although they practised a lot, •

independent **Clause**

• you have to work hard.

• I gave her my favourite toy.

• we drove to the concert instead.

• they lost the soccer game.

• she tries something new.

• we had fun at the beach.

C. **Fill in the blanks with the correct conjunctions to join the clauses.**

| if | because | and | while |

💡 **Conjunctions** are used to join clauses to make sentences.

1. We did not arrive in town on time _____ our car broke down on the way.

2. They watched some trailers _____ they were waiting for the movie to start.

3. I can give you a ride _____ you want to go to the mall.

4. Jonathan went trick-or-treating on Halloween night _____ he came home with lots of treats.

An **adjectival clause** gives information about a noun in a sentence.

An **adverbial clause** tells where or when the action of a verb takes place.

Examples

- The children, <u>who were hungry</u>, ate some cookies.   adjectival clause
- The players arrived <u>when the stadium was packed</u>.   adverbial clause

D. **Identify the clauses as adjectival or adverbial. Write "Adj." or "Adv." on the lines.**

1. The children played a board game <u>before they went to bed</u>.

   _____ Clause

2. The food, <u>which had gone bad in the fridge</u>, has been thrown away.

   _____ Clause

3. Mom told Benny to put the book back <u>where he had found it</u>.

   _____ Clause

4. The little geese follow my neigbour's dog <u>wherever it goes</u>.

   _____ Clause

5. My cousin, <u>who came from Prince George</u>, is enjoying her stay.

   _____ Clause

6. The bunch of flowers, <u>which Dad bought for Mom</u>, now sits beautifully in the vase.

   _____ Clause

7. Tom is the one <u>who always knows what to do</u>.

   _____ Clause

8. Mrs. Lowe cried <u>when she hurt her ankle</u>.

   _____ Clause

E. Add an adjectival clause or an adverbial clause to complete each sentence.

Adjectival Clause

1. This yo-yo, _____

    _____ , is my sister's.

2. The team, _____

    _____ , played very well.

3. The newspapers, _____ ,

    are a mess.

Adverbial Clause

1. Ben and June said hello _____

    _____ .

2. Jennifer is slowing down _____

    _____ .

3. The rabbits are having a race _____

    _____ .

Words that I Have Learned

_____

_____

_____

UNIT

13 Sentences

A **simple sentence** is formed whenever there is a subject and a verb. It expresses a complete thought.

Examples

- The dog chased the cat.
- Ron took out the garbage.

A. **Write simple sentences by putting the words in order.**

1. loves my winter in skiing family

   _____

2. sun morning the rises every

   _____

3. cat very Sophia's was lazy

   _____

4. we through drove Georgia

   _____

5. toward Catherine the quickly teddy walked bear

   _____

6. to Karen's everyone went yesterday party

   _____

7. Audrey very about was excited circus the

   _____

8. want cook Mrs. Stow not to did today

   _____

A **compound sentence** has two or more independent clauses.

Ron took out the garbage but he forgot the recycling bin. ← independent clauses

B. Underline the independent clauses in the compound sentences.

1. He is as strong as an ox but he would not hurt a flea.

2. I can go shopping tomorrow but I have to be home by 5 p.m.

3. I need to catch the next bus or I will have to walk to school.

4. Adam and Andrew studied very hard for their test and they are proud of their high marks.

5. The baseball game was cancelled today but the teams will play tomorrow.

6. We will catch a movie tonight or we will visit our friends.

C. Circle the correct conjunction. Then use it to rewrite each pair of sentences as a compound sentence.

A   and / or / but

I want to ride my bike.

It is raining outside.

B   and / or / but

I saw a shooting star.

I wished for a new piano!

A _____

_____

B _____

_____

A **complex sentence** has an independent clause and one or more dependent clauses.

Example

Ron took out the garbage
independent
because it is collection day tomorrow.
dependent

D. **Check the box if the dependent clause is underlined for each sentence. If not, put a cross and underline the dependent clause.**

1. <u>Wendy finished her new book</u> before it was time for bed. ☐

2. Lilian and Josephine have known each other <u>since they were in kindergarten</u>. ☐

3. Mel and Toby did not see the movie yesterday <u>because the tickets were sold out</u>. ☐

4. <u>The children played games in the doctor's office</u> while they were waiting for their turn. ☒

5. <u>Although Fabio likes tuna</u>, he does not like it with mayonnaise. ☐

6. If you do not give up, <u>you will succeed</u>. ☐

7. <u>Baby Jane kept crying</u> until Dad played with her. ☐

8. Jenny feeds her cat <u>whenever it is hungry</u>. ☐

9. Clark did well on his math test <u>because he studied all night</u>. ☐

10. <u>We will go cherry picking tomorrow</u> unless you have other suggestions. ☐

11. Wanda adopted a dog <u>after she discussed it with her mom</u>. ☐

E.   Identify the types of sentences. Check the correct circles.

	Simple	Compound	Complex
1.  Mia's parrot is very chatty.	◉	○	○
2. Robert likes to go swimming in the morning.	○	○	◉
3. I will go if she invites me.	○	◉	◉
4. Leave now or you will be late.	○	○	○
5. Florence was named after her mother.	◉	○	○
6. Mike would rather eat olives than pickles.	◉	○	○
7. Gaby has been collecting stamps since she was six.	○	○	○
8. They had fun even though the weather was bad.	○	○	◉
9. Luna will arrive today and she will leave next Sunday.	○	◉	○
10. Jenna likes playing in the band but she does not like the morning rehearsals.	○	◉	○

Words that I Have Learned

_____

_____

_____

UNIT
14 **Punctuation**

We use the **comma** (**,**) to indicate one or more pauses in a sentence.

If a sentence ending in a period is put inside quotation marks and is followed by an introductory clause, replace the period with a comma.

Examples

- Giraffes, raccoons, and dolphins are all mammals.
- "We are leaving," said Dad.

A. **Write the question numbers in the correct columns to indicate whether or not the commas in the sentences are in the correct places. Then rewrite the incorrect sentences with the correct punctuation.**

1. Samantha, Jack, and Grace went to the concert together.

2. Kevin can you, please help me?

3. Pepper my dog, knows, a lot of tricks.

4. "We will go to the museum this Sunday," said George.

5. "I am going for a walk", said Taylor.

6. Toby, please set the table first.

Correct Sentence	Incorrect Sentence	Rewritten Sentence
○	○	_____
○	○	_____
○	○	_____

The **colon** (:) is another punctuation mark used to indicate pauses in a sentence. It is used to join two separate sentences when the second explains the first, or to set off a concluding statement. The colon is also used to introduce a list of items.

Examples

- Ron is excited: he has finally finished his project.
- Family is more important than money: some things in life are irreplaceable.
- She ordered these items: paper, staplers, and glue.

B. **Add colons to the sentences where appropriate.**

Birthday List:
1. Telescope
2. Drawing pencils
3. New dress

1. Ivy has three items on her birthday list a telescope, drawing pencils, and a new dress.

2. There was one problem with Robert's plan he did not have enough money to buy the material.

3. Never take school for granted some children never get the chance to attend.

4. There are four foods Stephen does not like to eat beans, pork, salmon, and bananas.

5. Little Ava solved the puzzles within minutes intelligence is not determined by age.

6. I have read several genres of books drama, mystery, and science fiction.

C. **Write three sentences using the colon.**

1. _____

2. _____

3. _____

The **semicolon** (;) also indicates a pause in a sentence. It is used to join two separate sentences when the second elaborates on the first. It is also used to replace conjunctions such as "and", "but", "since", and "so".

Examples

• Our prices are wrong; we ordered from the old catalogue.

• Three people built the model; only one took credit for it.

D. Rewrite the sentences using semicolons where appropriate.

1. Daisy said she will be late for dinner she has an appointment.

    _____

2. The Mona Lisa is in Paris I will never see it in person.

    _____

3. We cannot wait much longer we will miss our bus.

    _____

4. It is not necessary to bring a gift it is your presence that is most desired.

    _____

5. The last city we visited was Prague it was my favourite.

    _____

6. Jeremy's backyard is large it is great for running around in.

    _____

    _____

7. It will rain tomorrow it will be good for the garden.

    _____

    _____

Weather Forecast

Shower

Tomorrow 60% rain

The **dash** (–) is yet another form of punctuation used to indicate a pause in a sentence. It is used to insert explanatory material.

Example

Understanding one's limitations – time, ability, and money – makes it easier to make plans in life.

E.   Add commas, colons, semicolons, and dashes to the story where appropriate.

Ms. Duncan's grade six class went to Kearney for a week-long trip in June. The kids learned a number of things: how to canoe; how to make dream catchers; and how to work in teams. One morning they stopped by a marsh to learn about insects that live in water. "Let's study these insects," Ms. Duncan said. The camp leaders were glad that every kid had brought insect repellent in tubes; aerosol cans are not good for the environment. Each evening, a leader named Mike would teach the kids a new song, one of which was called "The Merry Moose" so the kids could sing on their way back to their cabins afterwards. They also learned about everything they needed to build a campfire; matches, or a lighter, tinder, and kindling.

Words that I Have Learned

_____

_____

_____

A.   Circle the answers.

1.   The abstract noun "beauty" represents a/an _____ .

feeling

idea

quality

2.   Which sentence has the indirect object of a verb underlined?

Mary wrote <u>Dan</u> a letter.

<u>The movie</u> was interesting.

Dad made me <u>a sandwich</u>.

3.   Which sentence has the object pronoun underlined?

<u>They</u> skipped down the hill.

She always helped <u>them</u>.

<u>I</u> cannot believe him!

4.   Which type of pronoun is "himself"?

subject pronoun

object pronoun

reflexive pronoun

5.   Which modal verb is correct in the sentence below?

"_____ I stay up late?" asked Ali.

Would

Will

Can

6.   Which sentence uses the past progressive tense?

I read the book again.

Neel is sleeping soundly.

I was cooking when he called.

7.   Which tense is used in the sentence below?

I will be resting all day.

future progressive tense

present progressive tense

simple future tense

8.   Which tense is used in the sentence below?

Their team has won for years.

simple past tense

present perfect tense

past perfect tense

9.   Which word is not used with the perfect tense?

before

already

yesterday

10.   Which sentence is in the correct passive voice for the sentence below?

The cat broke the vase.

The vase is broken.

The vase was breaking.

The vase was broken.

11. Which sentence shows the indirect speech of the sentence below?

   "I love roses," Claire said.

   Claire said that I love roses.

   Claire said that she loved roses.

   Claire says that she loved roses.

12. The superlative form of the adjective "gigantic" is _____ .

   giganticest

   more gigantic

   most gigantic

13. An adjective that can be created from the verb "love" is _____ .

   loving

   more love

   lovingly

14. Which adverb form is correct in the sentence below?

   He is on time _____ than Aya.

   often

   more often

   most often

15. The noun phrase in the sentence below acts as _____ .

   Those are her keys.

   the subject

   the object

   the complement

16. Which sentence has the adverb phrase underlined?

   The room was really dark.

   Her new dress was bright red.

   Liam eats very loudly.

17. Which conjunction can join the clauses below?

   I was late _____ I got lost.

   because

   and

   if

18. Which sentence has the adverbial clause underlined?

   Daniel laughed when Chris fell.

   The car that I like is sold.

   He is the one who quit his job.

19. Which type of sentence is the sentence below?

   If you keep going, you will win.

   simple sentence

   compound sentence

   complex sentence

20. Which punctuation is correct in the sentence below?

   This is the list ( ) tins, pins, and bins.

   :

   ;

   –

Nouns, Direct and Indirect Objects, and Pronouns

B.   Read the story. Write the words in bold in the correct blanks. Then circle two direct objects and underline two indirect objects in the story.

The Garcias want to take a vacation. Mr. and Mrs. Garcia decide to take their son, Ivan, and their daughter, Marissa, camping in Sandbanks Provincial Park in **Ontario**. The **family** has taken a few vacations before but this will be their first **time** camping together. In fact, only Mr. Garcia has camped before.

Mr. Garcia starts to pack the car. The most important item is the **tent**. **He** packs clothing, sleeping bags, fishing gear, insect repellent, sunscreen, and games. Mrs. Garcia hands **him** pillows, a cooler, and the **water**. While he fits everything into the car, Mr. Garcia sends Ivan

and Marissa back into the house a few times. "Where **we** are going, you will not need those," he says as he hands Ivan his video games. "You won't need these either," he says to Marissa as he passes **her** the movies she wants to bring.

"Now hurry up," says Mrs. Garcia. "You are taking too long."

Ivan and Marissa wonder what they are getting **themselves** into.

N O U N			
	_____ countable noun	_____ proper noun	_____ abstract noun
	_____ uncountable noun	_____ collective noun	

P R O N O U N	**subject pronoun**	**object pronoun**	**reflexive pronoun**
	_____	_____	_____
	_____	_____	_____

Modal Verbs, Tenses, and Voice

C. **Underline the modal verbs. Then write "A" for ability, "PE" for permission, "PO" for possibility, and "RA" for requesting assistance above them to show their functions.**

The Garcias arrive at the campground and find their campsite by a lake. However, it looks like it could rain any minute, so Mr. Garcia, who cannot set up the tent alone, says, "Marissa, could you please lend me a hand?"

After setting up their tent, Mr. Garcia tells Ivan that he could go fishing with him at sunrise the next day. Ivan's jaw drops open in disappointment.

"Would you two gather some firewood for dinner?" asks Mrs. Garcia.

"Can we go home instead?" cries Marissa. She is already wishing she could watch a movie and she knows Ivan wants to play his video games.

"Seems like the clouds have parted," says Mrs. Garcia. "You two can go and play nearby after collecting firewood."

"You cannot miss dinner!" Mrs. Garcia shouts after them as they wearily make their way to the beach to look for firewood.

D. **Write the tense of each sentence in the box. Then rewrite the sentence in the passive voice.**

Tense

1. Ivan and Marissa saw a glistening object on the beach.

   _____

2. Ivan was carefully examining the object.

   _____

3. They will pick up the object gingerly.

   _____

Direct and Indirect Speech and Phrases

E. **Underline the introductory clauses and circle the reporting verbs. Then rewrite the sentences in indirect speech.**

1.   "We found something interesting on the beach!" Ivan told his parents.

_____

2.   Mr. Garcia exclaimed, "It is an antique brass bottle!"

_____

3.   "The bottle looks pretty," Mrs. Garcia said.

_____

4.   "It may have belonged to a pirate," Marissa guessed.

_____

F. **Write the types of phrases. Then fill in the blanks with the correct phrases.**

Type: _____ Phrase	Type: _____ Phrase
• Mr. and Mrs. Garcia • piece of paper	• very strange • delicately folded
Type: _____ Phrase	Type: _____ Phrase
• to pry it out	• finding out what is inside

1.   _____ are happy to see their children use their imaginations.

2.   The bottle makes a _____ sound when they shake it.

3.   _____ is the children's top priority!

4.   Ivan uses a twig _____ .

5.   It is a _____ _____ .

Clauses, Sentences, and Punctuation

G. **Identify the clauses as independent or dependent. Then match the clauses to form sentences.**

_____ Clause

_____ Clause

When the children opened it, •	• they decided to look there first.
If we can find the recipient, •	• they heard a little girl cry.
Although the sun was setting, •	• we can give the note back to her.
Because they had found it on the beach, •	• Ivan and Marissa headed out to search for the recipient.
As soon as they reached the beach, •	• the note said, "To my darling granddaughter."

H. **Add commas, semicolons, and dashes in the boxes. Then write the sentence numbers to indicate the types of sentences underlined.**

"Look! That little girl is crying ☐ " said Marissa. ❶ <u>"I'm going to help her."</u>

Approaching gently ☐ Marissa asked the girl ☐ "Why are you so sad?" "I've lost my grandma's brass bottle ☐ it was beautiful and unique ☐ " replied the girl.

"Don't be upset ☐ we found a brass bottle that contained a note. Here ☐ see if it's yours ☐ " offered Ivan ☐ giving her the bottle.

Types of Sentences
Simple: _____
Compound: _____
Complex: _____

❷ <u>Clara ☐ the little girl ☐ thanked them because it was her lost bottle!</u>

❸ <u>All the children played together and Ivan and Marissa could not help loving their camping vacation!</u>

Complete EnglishSmart (Grade 5)

Section 3

Vocabulary

UNIT

1 Nature Words

bedrock   cliff   fjord   glacial   island
landscape   mountain range   permafrost
scenery   tree line   tundra   vegetation

nature

Nunavut

Nunavut, Canada's newest territory, gets its name from the Inuktitut word meaning "our land". The vast region extends northwest from Hudson Bay beyond the tree line to the North Pole. The landscape is remarkably diverse. There are numerous islands throughout the region, with Baffin Island being the largest in Canada. The North Baffin region is a mixture of mountain ranges and fjords between high cliffs, while the Kivalliq area is flat. Arctic tundra covers most of Nunavut. Permafrost allows very few glacial plants to grow in the area. There is mainly a thin layer of soil on top of the bedrock, which is the solid rock layer beneath the surface layer of soil. For this reason, only a few varieties of rare berries, lichens, mosses, and small shrubs are part of the territory's vegetation.

Nunavut is a beautiful part of Canada with a large Inuit population. Although the scenery is breathtakingly beautiful, very few people find it comfortable as a place to call home due to the extremely low temperatures that affect people's lifestyles throughout the year. This is the main reason why Nunavut has the largest land area but is among the least populated of Canada's provinces and territories. Recently, however, the government of Canada has made significant efforts to encourage population growth and promote Nunavut's unique culture. For example, tourists have the options of enjoying the Arctic wildlife and learning about the Inuit culture. They can also stay in igloos and experience the marvellous Aurora Borealis up close!

A. Match the nature words with their meanings. Write the letters.

1. cliff _____

2. glacial _____

3. tree line _____

4. island _____

5. permafrost _____

6. landscape _____

7. bedrock _____

8. fjord _____

9. mountain range _____

A a long narrow inlet of sea between cliffs

B a thick permanently frozen soil layer

C a line of mountains connected by high ground

D icy

E a steep rock face

F edge of the area where trees can grow

G all the visible features of an area

H layer of rocks beneath the soil layer

I a piece of land surrounded by water

B. Unscramble the nature words. Then draw lines to match.

chienls _____

hssbru _____

olsi _____

riebers _____

druatn _____

smoses _____

yencesr _____

aruent _____

Nunavut's
_____
getionatVe

C. **Rewrite the sentences by replacing the underlined words with the correct nature words.**

> **More Nature Words**
>
> brook   compost   ice   icebergs   coast
> forest   terrain   boulder   plateau

1. <u>Large masses of ice</u> can detach from glaciers and float in the open water.

    _ice bulg_____

2. Because the <u>stretch of land</u> was too rocky, we decided not to go for a hike.

    _terrain_____

3. The town is isolated on a <u>level highland</u> projecting upward from the sea.

    _plateau_____

4. A <u>small stream</u> runs through the woods behind our school.

    _brook_____

5. <u>Decaying plant materials</u> can be used as nutrition for plants.

    _compost_____

6.   A <u>huge rock</u> fell from the mountain when the earthquake hit.

    _boulder_____

7. We are excited to have a picnic near a <u>large area covered with trees</u>.

    _____

8. <u>Frozen water</u> makes cars slip on roads and causes accidents.

    _ice_____

9. We made sandcastles along the <u>part of the land near the sea</u>.

    _coast_____

D. **Write sentences with the nature words.**

A glacial   **B** cliff

C boulder   **D** ice

E brook   **F** terrain

G vegetation **H** island

A _____

B _____

C _____

D _____

E _____

F _____

G _____

H _____

Words **that I Have Learned**

Nature Words

_____

_____

_____

_____

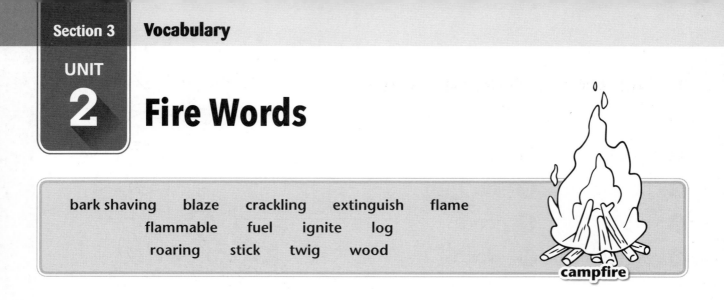

bark shaving   blaze   crackling   extinguish   flame
flammable   fuel   ignite   log
roaring   stick   twig   wood

campfire

Building a Campfire

Although sitting around a warm campfire is one of the great joys of camping, building a long-lasting, roaring campfire is not a simple task. Often, campers simply pile up a few twigs, add a couple of logs, stuff in a few rolls of newspaper, and ignite them. Unfortunately, they are disappointed when the fire blazes momentarily and is extinguished quickly.

Building a proper campfire requires technique. The first step is to gather numerous dry twigs and bark shavings and create a pile. Next, add small sticks around your pile in a tepee-like fashion. The tepee shape allows air, which the fire needs to maintain a flame, to get in underneath the pile. Build the pile by adding larger twigs and sticks but be sure to keep the tepee shape. Find an opening and ignite the dry bark shavings and twigs at the base of your pile. As the fire grows, add larger pieces of wood. These flammable materials will help keep you cozy for hours. Be careful not to simply toss logs onto the pile as it will flatten your tepee shape and no air will get in at the base. At this point, you should be enjoying a warm crackling blaze. Keep adding wood to maintain enough fuel to keep your fire going.

After building your campfire, gather around with your friends and drink some hot chocolate with marshmallows. It is the best way to enjoy a campfire. Apart from making s'mores, you can also share your favourite ghost stories or tell jokes and have a great time!

A. Check if the fire word is spelled correctly; put a cross if it is wrong and write the correct spelling beside the circle.

SPELLING

1. blase ⊗ blaze

2. log Ⓛ

3. crakling ⊗ crackling

4. raoring ⊗ roaring

5. flamme ⊗ flame

6. stick Ⓛ

7. wood ◯

8. feul ⊗ fuel

B. Circle the correct fire words to complete the sentences.

1. Campers usually just pile up a few **bark / twigs** and **ignite / crackle** .

2. The fire is weak. It might **extinguish / blaze** itself soon.

3. Keep adding **flame / wood** to maintain a good campfire.

4. Enough **ignite / fuel** is needed to keep a fire going.

5. Oil is a highly **flammable / roaring** liquid.

6. Bark **shavings / logs** catch fire easily but they burn out fast.

7. We roasted marshmallows over the **twig / campfire** .

8. Gasoline can cause a fire to **blaze / fuel** .

C.   **Circle the materials that can be used as fuel for a fire.**

magnet   sawdust   wood   glass

oil   coal   steel   rock   water

bark shavings   branches   cloth

coins   paper   logs   gasoline

propane   metal   plastic

D.   **Match to identify the fire words.**

Fire Word

Fire Type •

Fire Sound •

• campfire

• blaze

• crackle

• inferno

• wildfire

• roar

• snap

• bonfire

• sputter

• pop

• whoosh

• sizzle

E. **Fill in the blanks with the correct fire words.**

More Fire Words

heat   fireplace   fireworks   kindle

spark   torches   flickered

1. _____ are lit to brighten the dark passages of the dungeon.

2. A small _____ might be produced by striking two stones.

3. _____ from fire was essential for the survival of our ancestors.

4. The _____ makes the small restaurant warm and cozy.

5. The candles near the window

   _____ .

6. Dry twigs can _____

   a fire.

7. There were colourful

   _____ in celebration

   of Canada Day.

Words that I Have Learned

Fire Words

_____

_____

_____

_____

UNIT 3

Sport Words

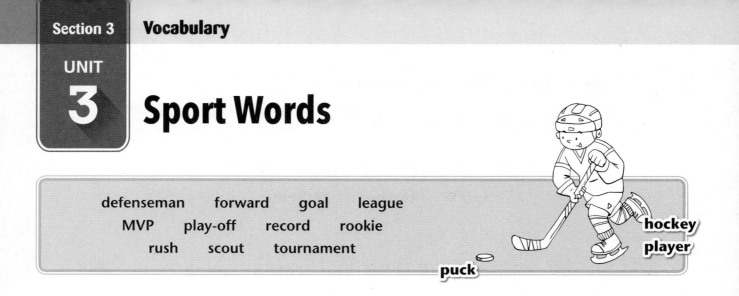

defenseman   forward   goal   league
MVP   play-off   record   rookie
rush   scout   tournament

hockey player

puck

A Legendary Hockey Player

With the retirement of Wayne Gretzky in 1999, there has been much speculation about who the greatest hockey player of all time is. Most hockey fans debate between Wayne Gretzky and Bobby Orr.

Not only did Bobby Orr break all the scoring records for a defenseman, he actually changed the way the game was played. Traditionally, before Orr's time, defensemen were big, slow players who seldom attacked the goal and only occasionally had a shot on goal. Their prime function was to defend their goal and move the puck up to the forwards. Bobby Orr changed all that with his exciting end-to-end rushes.

Orr was first spotted by scouts when he was just 12 years old. By the time he reached 15, he was distinguishing himself amongst 20-year-olds in one of the premier Canadian junior leagues. In 1966, his first year in the NHL, he won the Calder Trophy as Rookie of the Year. He went on to become the first player ever to win four awards in one season – the MVP, the leading point scorer, the best defenseman, and the play-off MVP. He was also the first defenseman to score 1000 points in a season.

Plagued by knee problems, Orr played only ten regular season games in 1975 but managed to play for Team Canada in 1976, and he was named the tournament MVP. By the 1978 season, Orr had undergone ten knee operations with no successful results, forcing him to retire at the ripe age of 30. One can only speculate as to what milestones Orr would have reached had he been able to continue playing hockey.

A. Draw lines to match the sport words with the definitions.

Sport Word

Definition

1. league
2. tournament
3. defenseman
4. rookie
5. MVP
6. play-off
7. scout

- player in a defensive position
- extra game played to determine the winner
- association of teams that play a sport and compete against one another
- first-year professional sports player
- sports competition
- talent evaluator for professional sports
- Most Valuable Player

B. Circle the correct sport words to complete the sentences.

1. Ana broke the **record / league** as the fastest swimmer in her school.

2. A **rookie / forward** on a soccer team is responsible for the team's scoring.

3. The spectators burst into cheers when the player scored a last-minute **goal / rush** .

4. The hockey **league / player** is famous for his end-to-end **rushes / records** .

5. The **puck / goal** moved so fast that I could barely see it.

6. The **MVPs / scouts** were evaluating the baseball players for the junior team.

C. **Match each sport with the equipment used to play it. Write the letters.**

basketball tennis gymnastics

hockey golf baseball

Sports Equipment

A bat

B puck

C springboard

D racket

E club

F basket

D. **Read the descriptions and name the sports.**

basketball   boxing   skiing   swimming

1. _skiing_

This sport is practised with skis on snow-covered mountains.

2. _basketball_

Points in this game are scored by getting the ball through a hoop called the "basket".

3. _swining_

This sport can be practised using different styles such as freestyle, breaststroke, butterfly, and backstroke.

4. _boxing_

Matches in this sport are held in "rings" and fights are decided by knockouts.

E. **Write to tell how your favourite sport is played. Use as many sport words as possible. Then draw the equipment used to play it.**

My Favourite Sport: Soccer

Equipment Used: ball

Number of Players: to 20

My Favourite Player: XXX

How the sport is played:

kick the ball to enemy's net to get point most point team win

It is my favourite sport because it is fun

Section 3

Vocabulary

Words that I Have Learned

Sport Words

UNIT

4 Personality Trait Words

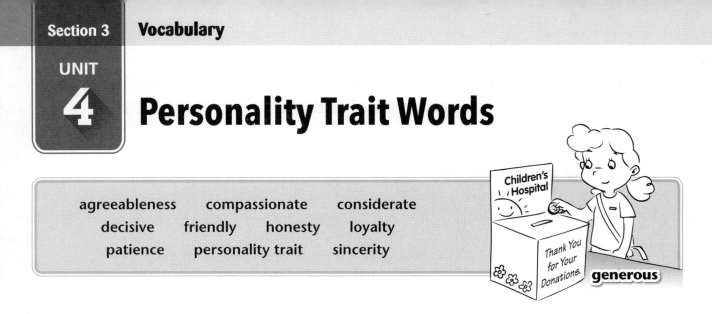

agreeableness   compassionate   considerate
decisive   friendly   honesty   loyalty
patience   personality trait   sincerity

generous

Summer Camp Champion

Mr. Dan finally announced that he had chosen this year's Sunshine Summer Camp Champion! He told all the children at the beginning of the self-improvement camp that he had a secret list of personality traits that he would look for in the winner.

When all the eager children gathered in the assembly hall, he said, "I will begin by saying how pleased I am with all of you for making such a great effort to become better people over the summer. You have all learned a lot here and now it's time to find out who possesses the traits of a winner! It was hard for me to decide on only one champion but I will explain how I made my decision.

This year's winner has agreeableness as she is a friendly, generous, and considerate young lady. Her honesty and loyalty are two of her many impressive characteristics. She is compassionate toward her friends and would not hurt anyone in order to win. She is very decisive as she had clearly decided to be on her best behaviour from the beginning and she was able to follow through. I'm glad to see how she always says "please" and "thank you". As each of you grows older, you will realize how these little things make you a better person. I will only suggest to Kinsley Brown to practise patience and wait for me to give her this year's trophy! You all deserve applause so there is a surprise waiting for you in the dining hall for your efforts and sincerity! Thank you!"

A. Write the personality trait word that has a similar meaning to the one in bold above each box. Then find the words in bold in the word search.

Personality Traits

pleasing   charitable   truthful   determined

amiable   faithful   caring   tolerant   thoughtful   genuine

agreeable

compassionate

considerate

decisive

friendly

honest

loyal

patient

sincere

generous

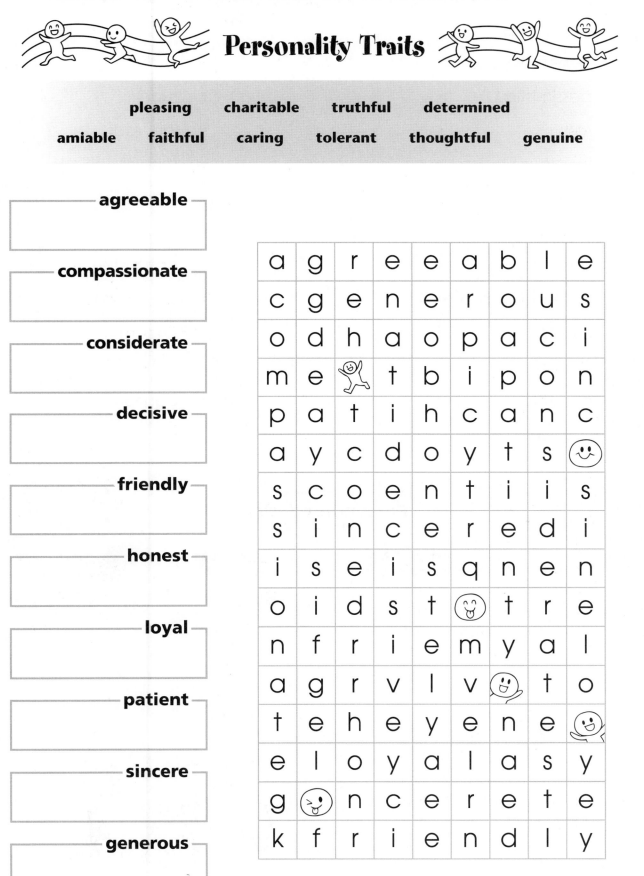

a	g	r	e	e	a	b	l	e
c	g	e	n	e	r	o	u	s
o	d	h	a	o	p	a	c	i
m	e		t	b	i	p	o	n
p	a	t	i	h	c	a	n	c
a	y	c	d	o	y	t	s	
s	c	o	e	n	t	i	i	s
s	i	n	c	e	r	e	d	i
i	s	e	i	s	q	n	e	n
o	i	d	s	t		t	r	e
n	f	r	i	e	m	y	a	l
a	g	r	v	l	v		t	o
t	e	h	e	y	e	n	e	
e	l	o	y	a	l	a	s	y
g		n	c	e	r	e	t	e
k	f	r	i	e	n	d	l	y

B.   **Draw lines to match the personality trait words with opposite meanings. Then write the words in the correct boxes.**

generous   •   •   gloomy

pessimistic   •   •   rude

rash   •   •   ignorant

hostile   •   •   miserly

courteous   •   •   indecisive

cowardly   •   •   lazy

cheerful   •   •   optimistic

knowledgeable   •   •   courageous

diligent   •   •   sincere

decisive   •   •   amicable

deceitful   •   •   cautious

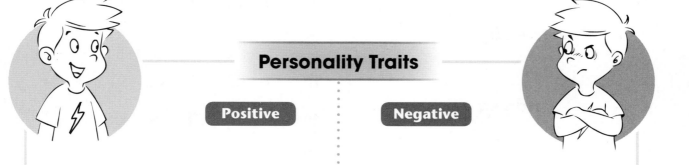

Personality Traits

Positive   **Negative**

C.   Fill in the blanks with the correct personality trait words.

thoughtful   courageous   optimistic

diligent   generous   determined   rude

1. Susan was _____ enough to face her fear of heights and learn tightrope walking.

2. No matter how difficult life is, Joshua always stays _____ .

3. The _____ boy pushed me aside as he ran to catch the bus.

4. Tammy was very _____ in giving me something that I really needed for my birthday.

5. The _____ baker donated bread to the homeless shelter.

6. Natalie is _____ to win the figure skating championship. She is _____ enough to practise every day.

Words that I Have Learned

Personality Trait Words

_____

_____

_____

_____

Disaster Words

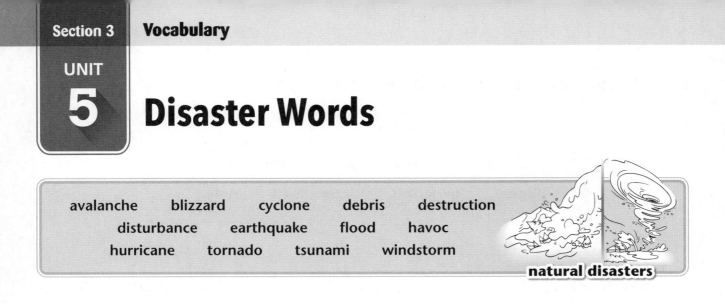

avalanche　blizzard　cyclone　debris　destruction
disturbance　earthquake　flood　havoc
hurricane　tornado　tsunami　windstorm

natural disasters

Types of Natural Disasters

A natural disaster is a major environmental event that can cause damage to property or loss of life. It is the result of disturbances in the natural processes of the Earth. Hurricanes are violent storms with fierce gusts of wind. Tornadoes and cyclones are also violent windstorms, usually with strong circular movements of wind.

Blizzards and avalanches are snow-related natural disasters. A blizzard is a severe snowstorm with extremely high winds. An avalanche occurs when large masses of snow, ice, and rock fall swiftly and in huge quantities down mountainsides. This results in extremely low visibility, unstable ground, and the threat of great destruction from falling debris.

Another serious type of natural disaster occurs when the Earth's water processes are out of control. Floods and tsunamis are such examples. A flood is caused by an overwhelming amount of water spilling onto dry land from large bodies of water such as rivers. This usually happens when there is a huge amount of rainfall in the area. A tsunami is an even bigger natural disaster that causes enormous waves as a result of an earthquake at the seabed. Earthquakes are sudden violent tremors of the ground.

Although these highly destructive natural disasters claim many lives and wreak environmental havoc around the world, most of them can be predicted by monitoring weather patterns and the Earth's natural processes. For example, scientists can forecast disturbing natural conditions by using devices such as satellites, seismometers, and global positioning systems. This enables city planners, engineers, and architects to build structures that minimize harm.

A. Write to group the disaster words in the correct columns.

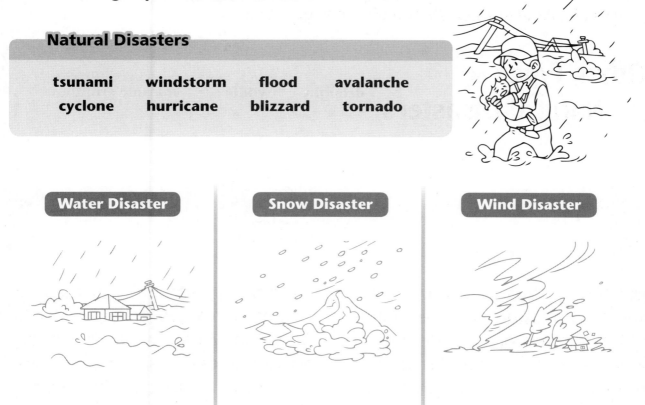

Natural Disasters

tsunami   windstorm   flood   avalanche
cyclone   hurricane   blizzard   tornado

Water Disaster	Snow Disaster	Wind Disaster

B. Write the name of the natural disaster for each picture. Then write a sentence using the disaster word.

1. _____

_____

2. _____

_____

3. _____

_____

C.　**Read the descriptions and label the disasters. Then research and write about one more type of natural disaster. Draw a picture to go with it.**

Other Types of Natural Disasters

drought　　wildfire　　volcanic eruption

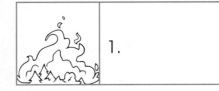

1.

This natural disaster occurs in the summer when lightning strikes a tree in a hot forested area. Even a small spark, under some conditions, can ignite into a raging fire. It can quickly spread to other areas as trees and dry vegetation burn easily, and can rapidly get out of control and cause great damage.

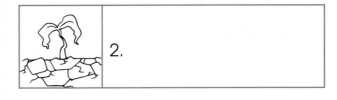

2.

This natural disaster results from the lack of rainfall over a long period of time. The dryness in the air and lack of water leads to loss of life and makes it hard for the crops in the area to survive. This is because crops, people, and animals all need water to live.

3.

A volcano, an opening in the Earth's surface that allows lava, gases, ash, and debris to escape from deep inside the Earth to its surface, can suddenly erupt and spread hot molten rock to the surrounding areas, destroying everything in its course, including lives.

4.

_____

_____

_____

_____

_____

_____

_____

D. Write the names of the natural disasters for the rescue options and safety precautions.

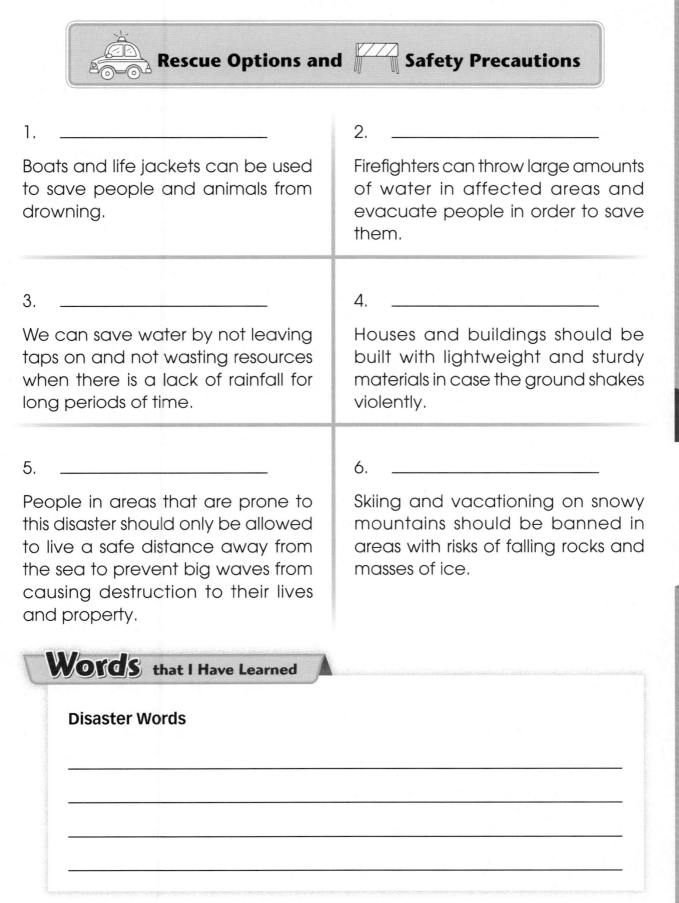

Rescue Options and **Safety Precautions**

1. _____

Boats and life jackets can be used to save people and animals from drowning.

2. _____

Firefighters can throw large amounts of water in affected areas and evacuate people in order to save them.

3. _____

We can save water by not leaving taps on and not wasting resources when there is a lack of rainfall for long periods of time.

4. _____

Houses and buildings should be built with lightweight and sturdy materials in case the ground shakes violently.

5. _____

People in areas that are prone to this disaster should only be allowed to live a safe distance away from the sea to prevent big waves from causing destruction to their lives and property.

6. _____

Skiing and vacationing on snowy mountains should be banned in areas with risks of falling rocks and masses of ice.

Words that I Have Learned

Disaster Words

_____

_____

_____

_____

UNIT 6 Astronomy Words

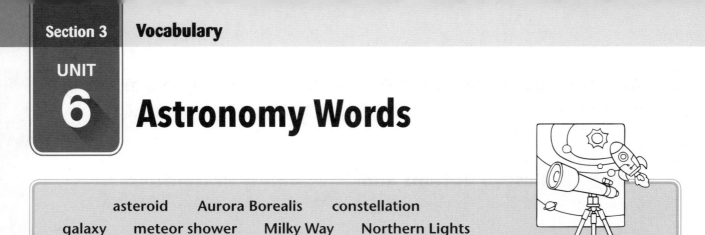

asteroid   Aurora Borealis   constellation

galaxy   meteor shower   Milky Way   Northern Lights

planet   shooting star   solar system   universe

astronomy

Exploring the Stars!

Dad and I bought a new telescope for our cottage last week! Before using it, we read a lot about our solar system, the different planets, asteroids, and so much more.

Dad told me that constellations are patterns of stars that ancient travellers used for navigation before there were maps. He also said that we, as Canadians, are extremely fortunate to experience the Aurora Borealis, which is also known as the Northern Lights. It is an absolutely majestic display of neon green, purple, and yellow lights lighting up the night sky! After learning all this, we plan to travel to Iqaluit, Nunavut to try and witness the Northern Lights together.

Even though I could go on mentioning the amazing and almost magical world of astronomy, I would like to write about my favourite part – the galaxies! A galaxy is a huge collection of gas, dust, and billions of stars. There are more than 100 billion galaxies in the universe and ours is called the Milky Way. It can be seen as a broad, bright band that stretches across the dark sky.

Another reason I love to study astronomy is that it helps my dad and me track and watch meteor showers in the summer months from our own backyard. They look like countless shooting stars across the night sky. I always make wishes on these shooting stars and the most amazing part is that most of my wishes have come true!

A.   Match the astronomy words with their meanings.

1.   Aurora Borealis •   • a pattern of stars

2.   constellation •   • the name of our galaxy

3.   astronomy •   • countless shooting stars

4.   meteor shower •   • the Northern Lights

5.   Milky Way •   • the study of stars and the universe

B.   Circle the correct astronomy words to complete the sentences.

1.   The **astronomy / solar system** is a part of the universe.

2.   The eight **planets / galaxies** and thousands of **asteroids / constellations** orbit the sun.

3.   Ancient travellers used the **constellations / shooting stars** for navigation.

4.   A **meteor / galaxy** is a huge collection of gas, dust, and stars.

5.   I always wish upon **galaxies / shooting stars** .

6.   How many wishes can you make when there is a **Milky Way / meteor shower** ?

7.   The **Northern Lights / Milky Way** can only be seen in the Northern Hemisphere.

C. **Unscramble the astronomy words and fill in the blanks. Use the diagram of the solar system.**

The Solar System

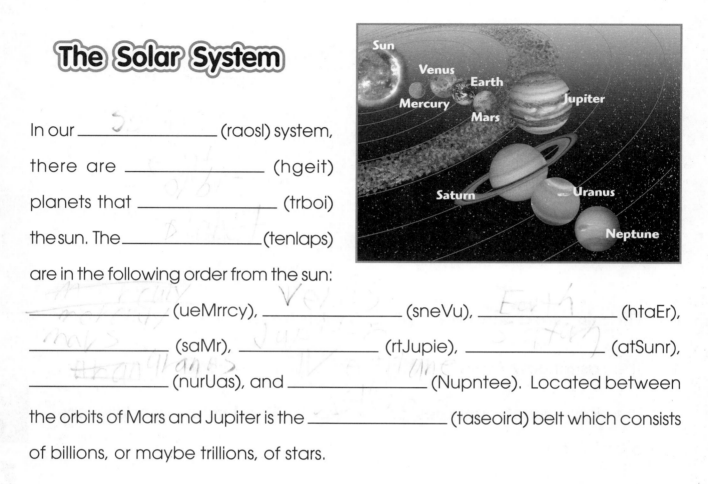

In our _____ (raosl) system,

there are _____ (hgeit)

planets that _____ (trboi)

the sun. The _____ (tenlaps)

are in the following order from the sun:

_____ (ueMrrcy), _____ (sneVu), _____ (htaEr),

_____ (saMr), _____ (rtJupie), _____ (atSunr),

_____ (nurUas), and _____ (Nupntee). Located between

the orbits of Mars and Jupiter is the _____ (taseoird) belt which consists

of billions, or maybe trillions, of stars.

D. **Match the astronomy words with their descriptions.**

1. astronaut •

2. comet •

3. rocket •

4. Big Dipper •

• a person who has undergone training in order to travel in a spacecraft

• a self-propelling device that can be launched into space

• an icy celestial object that orbits the sun and can be seen with a bright tail in the night sky

• a group of seven bright stars that resemble a dipper and can be used to locate Polaris (the North Star)

E. **Write the astronomy words in the correct groups.**

rocket   planet   sun   **Big Dipper**

Earth   galaxy   **Saturn**   telescope

constellation   **Milky Way**   comet

orbit   spacecraft   asteroid

Solar System	Group of Stars	Human-made Astronomy Device

Words that I Have Learned

Astronomy Words

_____

_____

_____

_____

UNIT 7

Feeling Words

ashamed   calm   confused   courageous

distressed   envious   jealous   kind

motivated   relieved   sad   shocked

proud

Kiera's Diary

Kiera recently started writing down her thoughts and feelings in her beautiful green diary. Her mother had told her that this was a good way of figuring out what to do when she was confused.

For example, on Monday, Kiera was sad, shocked, and envious when Susan won the award for "Best Writer". Kiera had worked so hard and contributed a lot of poems and stories to this competition.

However, on Tuesday, after she had written down her feelings, she was able to feel calm. She decided to befriend Susan and asked her for ways to improve her own writing skills. As they worked together, she was able to be kind and not jealous toward Susan by the end of the week.

I'm sorry, Emily.

Another problem arose on Wednesday when Kiera woke up to find that her cat, Fluff, was sick. Kiera was distressed at first but as Fluff got better by the end of the day, Kiera felt relieved.

On Thursday, Kiera got into an argument with her sister and felt ashamed when she realized that she should not have lost her temper. So she apologized to little Emily and gave her a hug before leaving for school.

When Friday came, her mother made Kiera her favourite cheesecake for being so thoughtful. Kiera was proud of herself and felt more courageous and motivated to become even better in the coming week!

A. Write the correct feeling words for the situations.

Feeling Words

ashamed	jealous	proud
shocked	relieved	confused
motivated	kind	distressed

Situation	**Feeling**
1. Jenna was caught stealing a piece of cake before the guests arrived.	_____
2. Andrew saw his mother give the bigger piece of pizza to his brother.	_____
3. Mr. Ali helped his neighbour's cat down the tree when it was scared.	_____
4. Cinderella could not fix her broken glass slipper in time for the party.	_____
5. Karen worked hard to land the lead role.	_____
6. Anna found her lost cat after searching for it for two days.	_____
7. Jack was walking happily down the mountain when he got hit by a ball.	_____
8. Nancy could not decide which necklace to buy for her upcoming graduation.	_____
9. After weeks of practice, Josh's hard work paid off when he won the athletic competition.	_____

Section 3

Vocabulary

B. Write the feeling words in the correct groups.

hopeful   agonized   confident   irritated   delighted

embarrassed   peaceful   grateful   hurt   upset

☺☺ **Positive Feeling** ☺☺   ☹☹ **Negative Feeling** ☹☹

C. Circle the correct synonym for the underlined feeling word in each sentence.

1. Julie was <u>satisfied</u> when she completed her lifesaving course.

   anxious

   contented

   interested

2. When Sandy applied for her new job, she felt <u>inferior</u> to the more experienced chefs.

   happier

   superior

   subordinate

3. 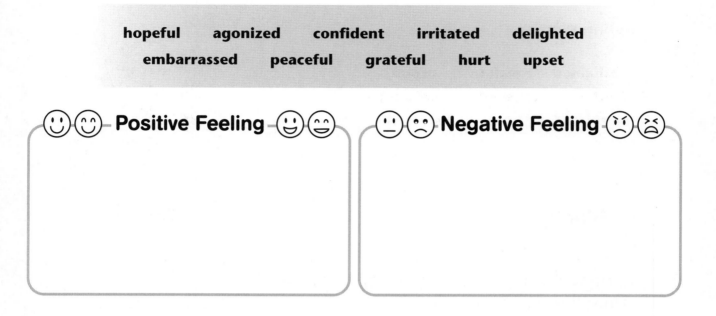 Danny was <u>frustrated</u> when he could not find his missing sock.

   exasperated

   delighted

   relieved

D. **Write sentences using the given feeling words.**

We're delighted!

1. delighted

   _____

2. frustrated

   _____

3. grateful

   _____

4. satisfied

   _____

5. exhausted

   _____

6. confident

   _____

7. hopeful

   _____

8. peaceful

   _____

Words that I Have Learned

Feeling Words

_____

_____

_____

_____

UNIT 8 Feline Words

bobcat   cheetah   claw   cougar
furry   jaguar   leopard   lion
lynx   pounce   purr   stalk   tiger

feline

Cats

When a house cat sits on your lap purring, it is hard to believe this cuddly, furry animal could belong to the same family as the sabre-toothed tiger. The first cat (dating back about 60 million years) was like the Miacis, a small weasel-like meat eater. This cat would not have resembled today's cat. The first cat-like ancestor, the Dinictis, dates back about 10 million years.

The early cat family was split into two distinct groups: sabre-toothed tigers and true cats. Sabre-toothed tigers were big, powerful animals that roamed the Earth for nearly 35 million years. They have been extinct for nearly 12 000 years. The second group, true cats, can be further divided into three categories: big cats (lions, tigers, jaguars, and leopards), small cats (felines), and cheetahs. The cheetah is the fastest animal on Earth; it is capable of speeds up to 100 km/h.

The small cat is a broad classification and includes the lynx, the bobcat, the cougar, and other similarly sized members.

Both big cats and small cats use similar methods of hunting. The leopard stalks its prey, and upon catching it, delivers a fatal bite, bringing quick death to its victim. A house cat lies in wait for an unsuspecting bird and then pounces on it or holds it with its claws and delivers the fatal bite.

A. **Unscramble and write the feline words. Then fill in the blanks with the correct words.**

Feline Words

gujaras

ounpecd

rurp

taskl

ceehhta

efeinl

uyfrr

waslc

1. The word " _____ " refers to a cat or other members of the cat family.

2. Lions, tigers, _____ , and leopards belong to the same category: big cats.

3. Almost all big cats roar but not _____ .

4. The _____ , which is capable of speeds up to 100 km/h, is the fastest animal on Earth.

5. Cats use their _____ for scratching, climbing, pouncing, and balancing.

6. Lions _____ their prey until they get close enough to attack it.

7. The cat _____ on the unsuspecting rat in the dark.

8. Adeline gently petted the _____ cat sleeping on her lap.

B. **Draw lines to identify the sounds that a house cat makes.**

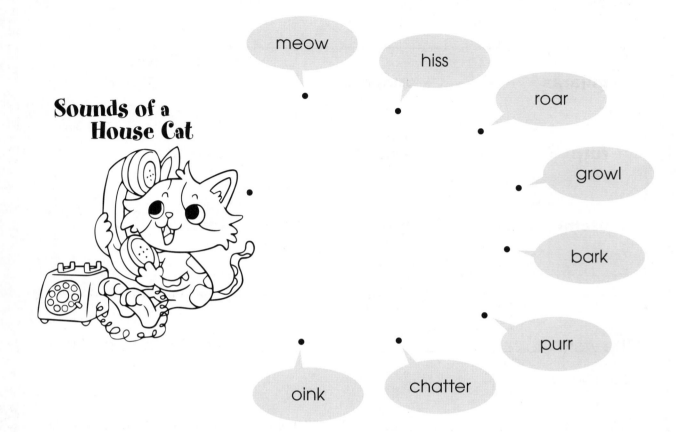

C. **Circle the feline words in the passage.**

There are many different members of the cat family. The snow leopard is able to camouflage in the white snow in the mountains of central Asia. Another popular member is a short-haired breed of domestic cat from Thailand, the Siamese cat. It is a long-bodied cat with slender legs and a long tail.

You would be interested to know that there are animals called "ligers". They have a lion and a tiger as their parents. Therefore, they carry the characteristics of both. Ligers also belong to the cat family. However, ligers are not found in the wild as much as pumas. The puma lives in a variety of habitats all over the world.

D. **Choose two members of the cat family. Draw them in the boxes and write their names. Then compare and contrast them using as many feline words as possible.**

Members of the Cat Family

Name:	Name:

How they are similar:

- _____
- _____
- _____
- _____

How they are different:

- _____
- _____
- _____
- _____

Words that I Have Learned

Feline Words

_____

_____

_____

_____

UNIT

9 **Animal Words**

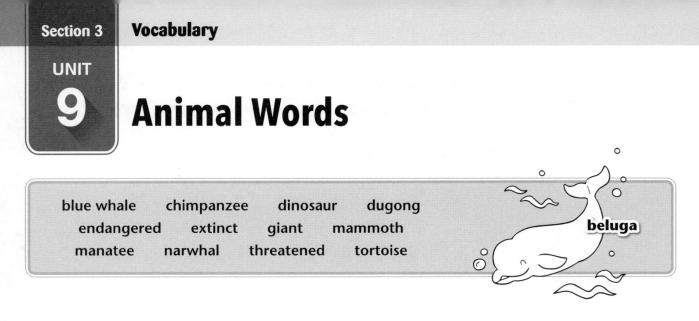

blue whale   chimpanzee   dinosaur   dugong
endangered   extinct   giant   mammoth
manatee   narwhal   threatened   tortoise

beluga

Animals in Peril

Animal activists and biologists have categorized the different species of animals in danger as being "near threatened", "vulnerable", "endangered", or "extinct".

The beluga is a type of extremely sociable whale. It has been classified as near threatened because although its population is not diminishing too rapidly right now, its numbers are under threat and have to be carefully monitored. The narwhal is also a sea animal that belongs to the same category. This small arctic whale has a spiraled tusk on its head that looks like a unicorn's horn.

Another category includes vulnerable animals. These species are at high risk of extinction but not in the near future. One example is the giant tortoise that has a dome-shaped shell and a long neck. Another is the dugong, a sea mammal that looks like a manatee.

Even more at risk are the endangered animals. These animals face a high risk of extinction in the near future. The blue whale, which is the largest animal on the planet, falls into this category. Another animal on this list is the chimpanzee, which is a very sociable animal that possesses more human-like characteristics than any other animals. Sadly, both these animals are now at risk.

Dinosaurs are extinct animals!

The biggest loss, however, are the animals that are already extinct because we will never get a chance to see them! There are no living members of these species. Dinosaurs and mammoths are examples of extinct animals.

With the long list of animals in peril, animal rights activists are trying to spread awareness and are asking for the public's help in order to protect all animals for generations to come.

A. Unscramble the animal words to complete the crossword puzzle.

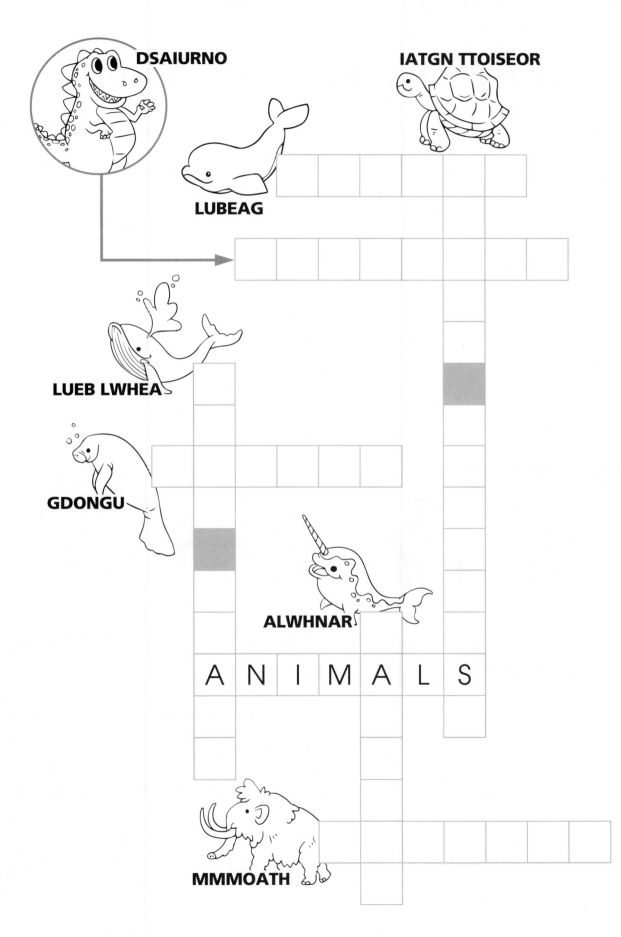

DSAIURNO

IATGN TTOISEOR

LUBEAG

LUEB LWHEA

GDONGU

ALWHNAR

A N I M A L S

MMMOATH

B.   **Write the correct labels for the groups of animals. Then research and add one example to each group.**

| Endangered | Near Threatened | Extinct | Vulnerable |

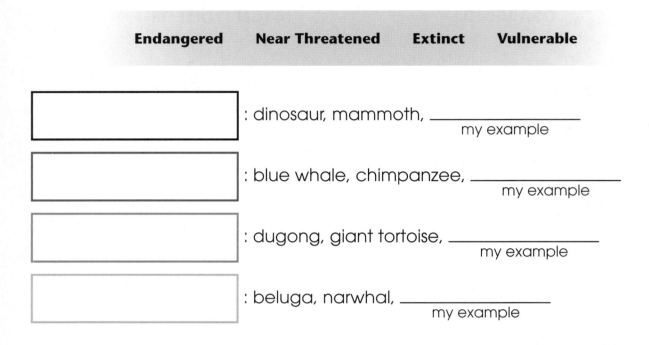

[   ] : dinosaur, mammoth, _____
                                    my example

[   ] : blue whale, chimpanzee, _____
                                    my example

[   ] : dugong, giant tortoise, _____
                                    my example

[   ] : beluga, narwhal, _____
                                    my example

C.   **Fill in the blanks with the correct animal words.**

More Animals in Peril

Malayan tiger   giant panda   orangutan   sea lion

1.   The _____ , which has reddish fur and lives in trees, is critically endangered.

2.   The _____ is also a critically endangered animal. It can only be found on the Malay Peninsula and in Thailand.

3.   The _____ is endangered because of the effects of climate change on ocean currents.

4.   The vulnerable _____ is a peaceful animal that is considered a national treasure in China.

D. **Draw and write about an animal in peril.**

An Animal in Peril

Animal: _____

Habitat: _____

Population: _____

Status: Near Threatened / Vulnerable / Endangered / Extinct

Physical Characteristics: _____

_____

It is endangered because _____

_____

Steps we could take to help its population:

_____

_____

_____

Words that I Have Learned

Animal Words

_____

_____

_____

_____

UNIT

10 Medical Words

antibiotic	chill	epidemic	fever
flu shot	headache	infection	influenza
pneumonia	symptom	treatment	vaccine	virus

medicine

Influenza

Typically, during winter months, many people come down with what is commonly called the "flu". Often, the symptoms will include fever, chills, headaches, and body aches. A person may feel aches in many of his or her joints and experience a loss of appetite.

Usually, an influenza attack lasts from four days to two weeks, and although uncomfortable, it does not cause great harm. However, some influenza viruses can be more serious. The influenza virus, depending on the strain, can weaken the body to the point where pneumonia and other diseases can set in.

From 1918 to 1919, a worldwide influenza epidemic killed 25 million people. This particular strain was one of the five deadliest epidemics of all time. But during that time, there was no scientific treatment for the infection. Today, antibiotics, a type of medicine, can protect people from developing pneumonia and other diseases that can follow the flu. Doctors have developed vaccines that can protect people against flu viruses. However, the strains of flu are constantly changing and it is difficult for doctors to keep up with the new strains of influenza that spread around the world.

The concern over influenza is so great that the Centers for Disease Control and Prevention (CDC) has created a special department to stay on alert to report any new strains of flu the moment they arise. Today, doctors are encouraging people to take flu shots. Although flu shots may not prevent the flu, they could significantly lessen the impact of the virus.

A. Check the correct meanings of the medical words.

1. symptom

   ☐ a disease
   ☐ a sign of disease

2. pneumonia

   ☐ a heart infection
   ☐ a lung infection

3. flu shot

   ☐ a type of virus
   ☐ a type of vaccine

4. treatment

   ☐ medical care given for an illness
   ☐ prevention of an illness

5. infection

   ☐ a disease caused by germs or bacteria
   ☐ a disease caused by antibiotics

6. fever

   ☐ an abnormally high body temperature
   ☐ an abnormally low body temperature

7. epidemic

   ☐ a cure for a disease
   ☐ an outbreak of an infectious disease

8. chill

   ☐ heat accompanied by sweating
   ☐ coldness accompanied by shivering

9. vaccine

   ☐ a substance injected to prevent a disease
   ☐ a substance taken to cure headaches

B. Draw lines to tell whether the medical words refer to symptoms or prevention or treatment.

Influenza

fever   •

chills   •

vaccine   •   • **Symptom**

headaches   •

flu shot   •

antibiotics   •

body aches   •   • **Prevention**
                                           or Treatment
loss of appetite •

C. Write the flu symptoms under the correct pictures.

More Flu Symptoms
cough
fatigue
sneezing
runny nose
sore throat

1. _____

2. _____

3. _____

4. _____

5. _____

D. Unscramble the medical words and fill in the blanks.

The word "flu" is often used as a short form of the word 1._____ .
flenuinza

2._____ of influenza may include aches, 3._____ ,
Sptsyomm   _illsch_

fever, and 4._____ . 5._____ , a sore 6._____ ,
ouchg   _nezeSgin_   _otrhat_

and a runny 7._____ are also common flu symptoms. Severe
sone

influenza viruses may lead to 8._____ or other diseases.
nimoanpeu

A worldwide influenza 9._____ in 1919 caused 25 million deaths
pideecmi

because there was no scientific 10._____ available. Today,
reattenmt

11._____ are used to fight against
botiianscti

the development of more serious diseases.

To protect people against 12._____ ,
rsviuse

scientists have developed 13._____ .
aincevcs

There are flu 14._____ available to the
htsos

general public to control infection.

Words that I Have Learned

Medical Words

_____

_____

_____

_____

UNIT 11 Archaeology Words

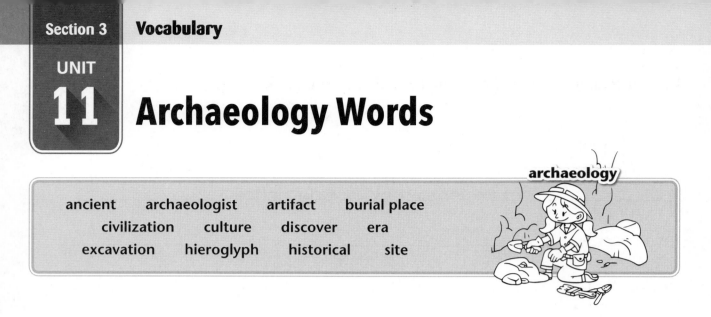

archaeology

ancient   archaeologist   artifact   burial place
civilization   culture   discover   era
excavation   hieroglyph   historical   site

Ancient Egyptians

The ancient Egyptians lived in the northeast corner of Africa, which is known today as Egypt. It is situated along the river Nile and this location helped provide the civilization with the means for agriculture, transportation, and a rich culture.

Most of us are familiar with the hieroglyphs found in Egyptian pyramids from that era. They are the characters of the ancient Egyptian writing system. Hieroglyphs prove that the people of ancient Egypt were interested in recording and communicating their laws, traditions, and beliefs. Additionally, archaeologists – people who study historical civilizations by recovering cultural materials – have discovered many artifacts in the area through excavations. Excavation is the process of digging and recording the findings in an area. The area being excavated is called a site.

The ancient Egyptians were ahead of their time. They achieved great success in the areas of technology, medicine, and mathematics. They also made ceramics and eating utensils. We know this today by studying history. However, their greatest achievement is definitely the majestic pyramids. They were built as burial places for Egyptian rulers called pharaohs. It is believed that labourers were able to build the pyramids by wetting the sand that covers the entire area in order to drag heavy stones across it. The Great Pyramid of Giza is one of the seven wonders of the ancient world.

A. Write the letters to match the archaeology words with their meanings.

Archaeology Word

1. ancient _____
2. archaeologist _____
3. artifact _____
4. civilization _____
5. culture _____
6. discover _____
7. era _____
8. excavation _____
9. history _____
10. site _____

Meaning

A human-made object of historical or archaeological interest

B distinct period of history

C of or from the distant past

D find

E the process of digging, especially for archaeological purposes

F the customs and beliefs of people

G person who studies human history through ancient objects

H advanced human society with well-developed social organizations

I ground on which something is located

J the study of past events

B. Fill in the blanks with the correct archaeology words.

What Archaeologists Do

| classify | excavate | analyze | present | survey | write |

1. _____ : examine areas in search of archaeological sites

2. _____ : dig a site to find ancient remains

3. _____ : arrange findings in groups or categories

4. _____ : study and classify artifacts

5. _____ : work on reports, papers, and articles for publication

6. _____ : give presentations on findings

C.   Read the uses and identify the archaeology tools.

Archaeology Tools

screen	clippers	mattock	trowel
file	shovel	brush	tape measure

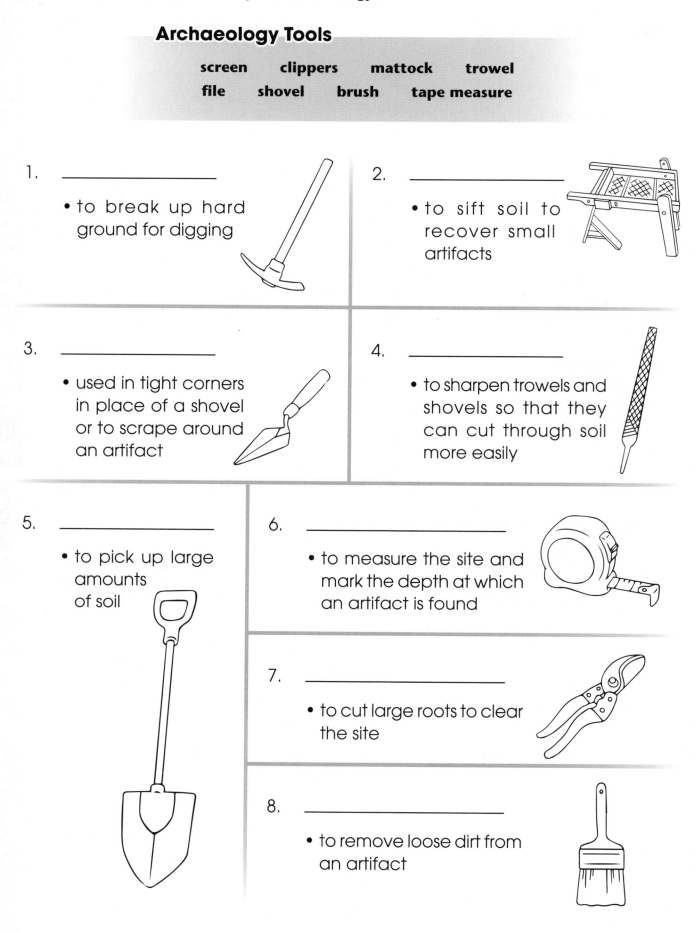

1. _____
   - to break up hard ground for digging

2. _____
   - to sift soil to recover small artifacts

3. _____
   - used in tight corners in place of a shovel or to scrape around an artifact

4. _____
   - to sharpen trowels and shovels so that they can cut through soil more easily

5. _____
   - to pick up large amounts of soil

6. _____
   - to measure the site and mark the depth at which an artifact is found

7. _____
   - to cut large roots to clear the site

8. _____
   - to remove loose dirt from an artifact

D. **Fill in the blanks with the correct archaeology words.**

> **More Archaeology Words**
>
> prehistoric   conservation   earth   museum
> relics   repairing   fossils   cavemen   remains

1. Pictures drawn by _____ were discovered on the site.

2. _____ show the existence of dinosaurs in _____ times.

3. Archaeologists dig up the _____ to look for the _____ of buried civilizations.

4. The artifacts from the excavation are now on display at the _____ .

5. The preserved tombs are important _____ of ancient Egypt.

6. The _____ of artifacts includes stabilizing, preserving, _____ , and reconstructing the artifacts.

Words that I Have Learned

Archaeology Words

_____

_____

_____

_____

UNIT 12 Communication Words

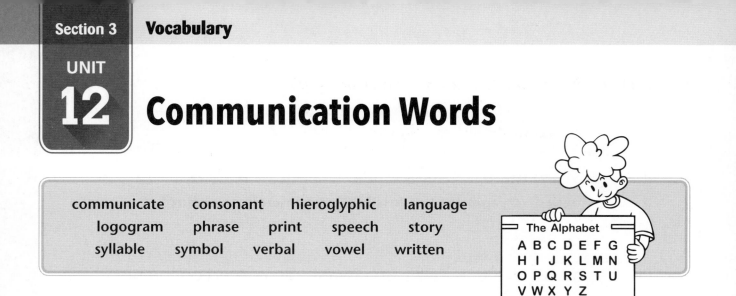

communicate   consonant   hieroglyphic   language
logogram   phrase   print   speech   story
syllable   symbol   verbal   vowel   written

The Alphabet
A B C D E F G
H I J K L M N
O P Q R S T U
V W X Y Z

The Origins of Written Words

By the age of six or seven, most schoolchildren around the world are able to print words and begin to create stories. By this time, they have already mastered speech and can communicate their thoughts effectively. Can you imagine a world without verbal and written communication? Like most things in the civilized world, language was part of an evolutionary process.

Early people, known as Homo sapiens, communicated by drawing pictures on the walls of caves. They would draw pictures of their hunts for food and of important social and personal family events. It was not until 3000 BCE that actual writing, a method of recording language sounds, came into being. Early forms of writing were traced back to the Sumerians of Mesopotamia. Their writing was made up of symbols called logograms that stood for words or phrases. This system evolved to include representations of syllables. Thus the Sumerians were using both logograms and syllabic forms to create writing.

To avoid confusion, sounds, such as the vowel and the consonant sounds that we use today, were given specific symbols. This was the early creation of an alphabetic system. There are not many symbols needed to create a language. For example, the English language uses an alphabet with only 26 letters but there are over 500 000 English words listed in the Oxford English Dictionary.

The Egyptians developed hieroglyphics, a system of writing, approximately a hundred years after the Sumerian system. Many forms of writing were adapted by other peoples until about 1500 BCE when a partially alphabetic system was created. This marked the early stages of writing as we know it today. The Greeks are credited with having separated vowel and consonant sounds by 750 BCE, thereby creating the fully alphabetic system, which paved the way for the full development of organized language.

A. Write the communication words in the correct groups.

consonant   hieroglyph   language   logogram   print

speech   story   syllable   symbol   vowel

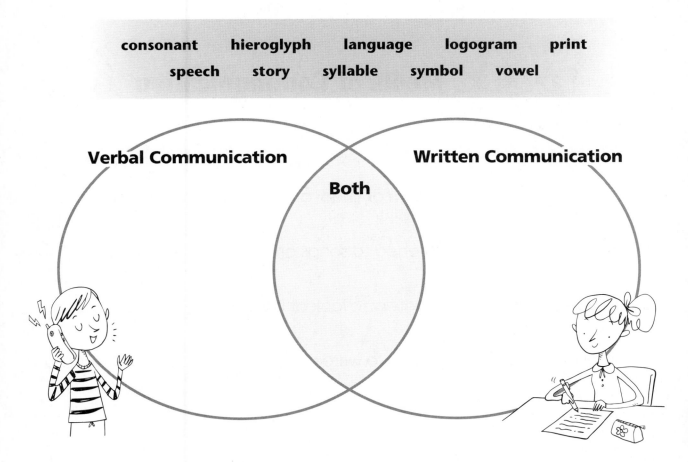

Verbal Communication

Written Communication

Both

B. Match the communication words with their definitions.

Communication Word

Definition

• a mark used to represent an object

1. phrase •

• a basic speech sound that is not a vowel

2. consonant •

3. symbol •

• a small group of words as a unit

4. verbal •

• a structured system of words or signs for communication

5. written •

• expressed in spoken words

6. print •

• expressed in writing

7. language •

• clearly written text

8. hieroglyphics •

• an ancient system of writing

C.   Fill in the blanks with the correct communication words.

Media of Communication

1.   _____ is a medium of visual and verbal communication.
      Television/Radio

2.   Many years ago, people listened to songs on _____ .
      radios/walkie-talkies

3.   We recently went to an art gallery to look at beautiful _____ .
      pets/paintings

4.   My sister and I had enough time to write a _____ to Grandma
      letter/alphabet
      before dinner.

5.   My father likes reading the _____
      newspaper/phone
      every morning.

6.   Jake was making dinner when his
      _____ rang.
      television/phone

7.   The reporter researched
      information on the _____ for his new article.
      telegraph/Internet

8.   I sent my teacher an _____ to explain my absence.
      writing/e-mail

9.   My father took a _____ of the snowy mountains.
      photograph/notice

10.   My mom likes flipping through _____ while waiting at the
      magazines/podcasts
      doctor's office.

D. **Match the methods of communication with the tools used to communicate.**

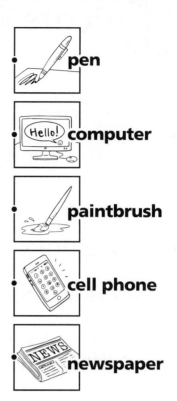

1. painting •
2. texting •
3. news •
4. writing •
5. e-mail •

• pen

• computer

• paintbrush

• cell phone

• newspaper

E. **Write about your favourite method of communication.**

_____

_____

_____

_____

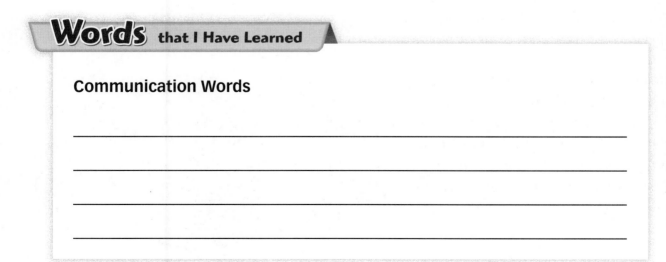

Words that I Have Learned

Communication Words

_____

_____

_____

_____

UNIT 13 Genre Words

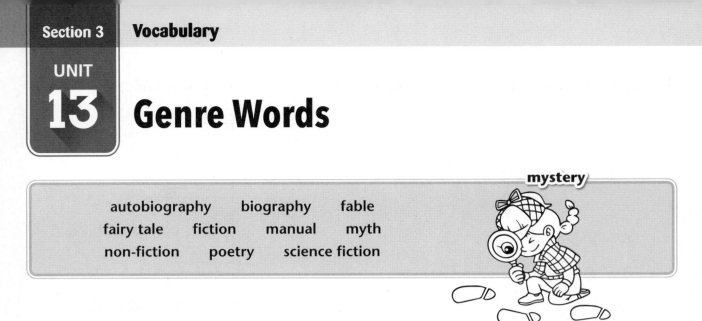

autobiography   biography   fable
fairy tale   fiction   manual   myth
non-fiction   poetry   science fiction

mystery

Genres of Books

Mrs. Lee's class was having an extremely hard time deciding which book to read for the week's library lesson. "I want to suggest a mystery novel because it contains many interesting secrets and is full of suspense! We can have fun solving the mystery together before we reach the end of the story," said Michael.

"I like science fiction!" Alana declared excitedly. "It usually contains stories of imaginary scientific advancements and I enjoy reading about aliens and robots living on other planets."

Suddenly, the children's discussion was interrupted by Mr. Jemison, the librarian, who said, "All the different types of books fall under two main categories: fiction and non-fiction. A biography is a factual written account of a person's life, so it is non-fiction. An autobiography is like a biography but it is about the writer's own life. A manual gives information and instructions so it is non-fiction too. Poetry, fables, fairy tales, and myths are all examples of fiction. Michael and Alana mentioned mystery and science fiction and these fall under the category of fiction as well. No matter what you choose, I would ask you to consider reading a different genre each week. So now that you know more about the different genres, it's time to decide whether you are interested in reading about real people and events or fantasy tales about imaginary lands."

The class was excited to pick out the book for the week and was thrilled when "The Awesome Adventures of Pegasus" was selected! It is a Greek myth about a flying horse which is said to still be seen as a constellation in the sky.

A. Unscramble the genre words. Then read the quotes from various books and identify their genres. Write the letters.

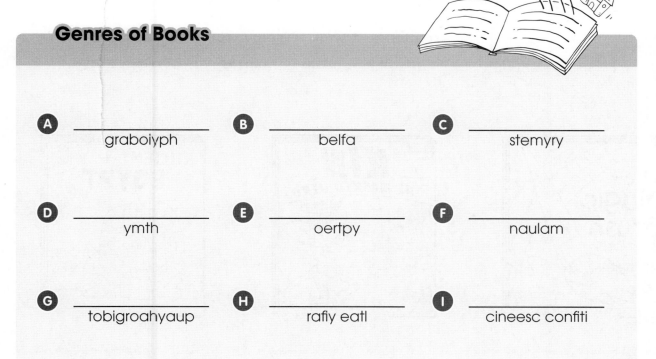

Genres of Books

A _____ graboiyph

B _____ belfa

C _____ stemyry

D _____ ymth

E _____ oertpy

F _____ naulam

G _____ tobigroahyaup

H _____ rafiy eatl

I _____ cineesc confiti

Quote	**Genre**
1. I need to follow the clues to find the culprit.	_____
2. The alien landed on the surface of the moon.	_____
3. As a child, I used to love the ice cream truck.	_____
4. With a wave of her wand, the fairy turned herself into a quill.	_____
5. Plug the power cord into a grounded outlet.	_____
6. Her life was full of periods of grief and happiness.	_____
7. The cat learned the lesson and promised never to be selfish again.	_____
8. Aurora, the goddess of dawn, cried and her tears became morning dew.	_____
9. I jump and I fly, In the clouds floating by.	_____

B.   Identify and write the genres of books.

Genres of Books

comics   travel   romance   cookbook

history   atlas   fantasy   horror

C. **Identify the genres of books as fiction or non-fiction. Write the words in the correct boxes.**

atlas   autobiography   biography   comics
cookbook   fable   fairy tale   fantasy
history   horror   manual   mystery   myth
romance   science fiction   travel

Genres of Books

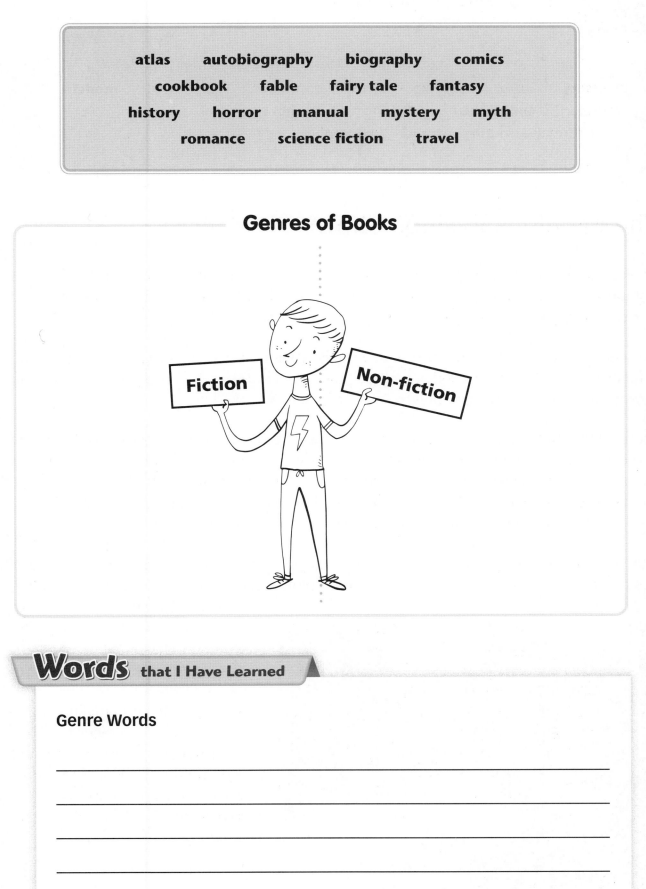

Fiction

Non-fiction

Words that I Have Learned

Genre Words

_____

_____

_____

_____

UNIT 14 Fashion Words

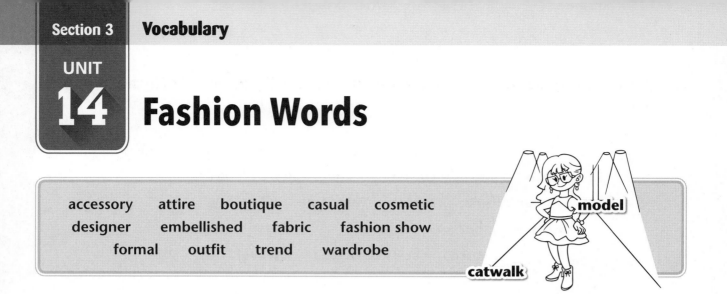

accessory   attire   boutique   casual   cosmetic
designer   embellished   fabric   fashion show
formal   outfit   trend   wardrobe

model

catwalk

The Fabulous Fashion Show

My aunt Carla wants to open her own boutique. She said the first step is to attend a local fashion show to find out what kind of clothes people like. So we attended a show and had an exhilarating evening discovering all of the latest trends!

We were excited to try on various accessories such as exotic silk scarves, high-end sunglasses, and hand-crafted jewellery and wristwatches. There was a huge wall showcasing brightly lit glass shelves full of cosmetics.

I noticed that tailors, designers, and fashion magazine editors were seated in the front row of the auditorium where the show was held. We were seated next to the long catwalk. It is a platform on which the models wearing the designers' clothes walk in order to display them to the audience. One by one, they walked in beautiful brocade dresses embellished with sequins and semi-precious stones such as jade and amethyst.

This was followed by a segment focusing on formal office attire and casual work outfits. For this, the models wore tailored suits in neutral colours like black, white, navy, and brown.

The fabrics and the sewing of the outfits were so carefully planned that I felt inspired to dress up like them in the future.

I had so much fun making notes on my favourite pieces. Upon returning home, Aunt Carla and I pretended to be supermodels ourselves and displayed our wardrobes for the whole family to enjoy!

A. Circle 14 fashion words in the word search.

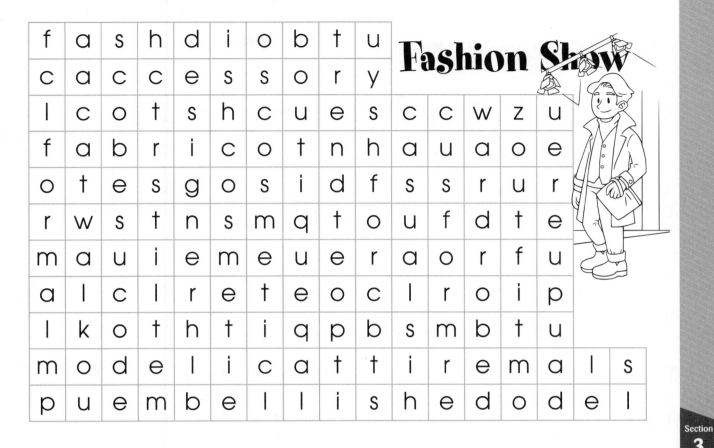

f	a	s	h	d	i	o	b	t	u			
c	a	c	c	e	s	s	o	r	y			
l	c	o	t	s	h	c	u	e	s	c	c	w	z	u
f	a	b	r	i	c	o	t	n	h	a	u	a	o	e
o	t	e	s	g	o	s	i	d	f	s	s	r	u	r
r	w	s	t	n	s	m	q	t	o	u	f	d	t	e
m	a	u	i	e	m	e	u	e	r	a	o	r	f	u
a	l	c	l	r	e	t	e	o	c	l	r	o	i	p
l	k	o	t	h	t	i	q	p	b	s	m	b	t	u
m	o	d	e	l	i	c	a	t	t	i	r	e	m	a	l	s
p	u	e	m	b	e	l	l	i	s	h	e	d	o	d	e	l

Fashion Show

B. Write the correct headings for the groups of fashion words.

> **Fashion Show**   **Clothing**   **Accessory**   **Professional**

1. _____

   brocade dress
   tailored suit
   formal office attire
   casual work outfit

2. _____

   scarf   wristwatch
   jewellery   sunglasses

3. _____

   model
   catwalk

4. _____

   tailor   designer   fashion magazine editor

C. Unscramble the fashion words and fill in the blanks.

1. Jade bought the perfect _____ for her outfit.
   ssaeorisecc

2. The celebrity has hired a renowned _____ to upgrade her
   gerdisen

   _____ .
   boredraw

3. Mom's favourite blouse is the one _____ with sequins and
   misheblleed

   crystals.

4. The _____ of this dress is so soft and luxurious!
   crabif

5. The editors of the magazine researched the latest fashion

   _____ from across the world.
   drenst

6. All employees are required to wear formal _____ to the
   tireat

   company's annual charity event.

7. My sister displays all her _____
   mesoticcs

   on her new dresser.

8. Maggie likes wearing _____
   slacua

   clothing on the weekends.

9. Look! That _____ on the
   lodem

   _____ is probably taller than
   twackla

   anyone I have ever met!

D. **Rewrite the sentences by replacing the underlined words with the correct fashion words.**

More Fashion Words

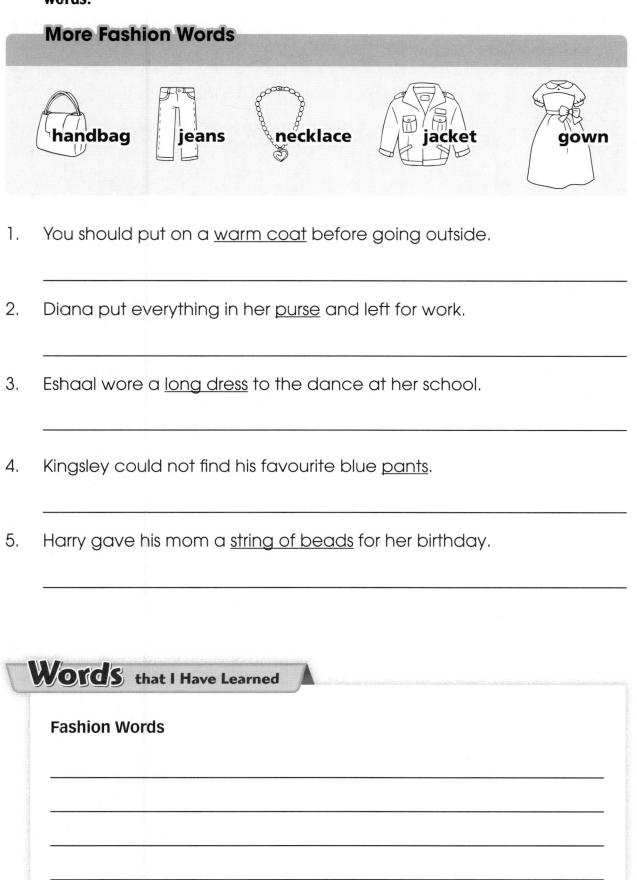

handbag   jeans   necklace   jacket   gown

1. You should put on a <u>warm coat</u> before going outside.

   _____

2. Diana put everything in her <u>purse</u> and left for work.

   _____

3. Eshaal wore a <u>long dress</u> to the dance at her school.

   _____

4. Kingsley could not find his favourite blue <u>pants</u>.

   _____

5. Harry gave his mom a <u>string of beads</u> for her birthday.

   _____

Words that I Have Learned

Fashion Words

_____

_____

_____

_____

A.   Circle the answers.

1.   Which nature word means "a steep rock face"?

island

fjord

cliff *(circled)*

2.   Which is not a type of fire?

fireplace *(circled)*

bonfire

inferno

3.   Which sport is played with a bat?

golf

tennis

baseball *(circled)*

4.   Loyalty and sincerity are both _____ words.

personality trait *(circled)*

medical

communication

5.   What does "considerate" mean?

patient

decisive

caring *(circled)*

6.   Which is not a natural disaster?

earthquake

influenza *(circled)*

volcanic eruption

7.   Which is a wind disaster?

cyclone *(circled)*

blizzard

flood

8.   Which is spelled correctly?

telscope

telescop

telescope *(circled)*

9.   Which is a negative feeling?

grateful

agonized *(circled)*

confident

10.   What feline is this?

tiger

lion

leopard *(circled)*

11. What do felines do when they hunt?

    stalk

    meow

    whoosh

12. Which animal is not extinct?

    manatee

    mammoth

    dinosaur

13. Which is used to prevent a disease?

    antibiotics

    vaccine

    medicine

14. Which is not a disease?

    influenza

    pneumonia

    body aches

15. A/An "_____" is an outbreak of an infectious disease.

    infection

    epidemic

    fatigue

16. What archaeology tool is this?

    mattock

    clippers

    trowel

17. What does an archaeologist do?

    excavate, classify, analyze

    sing, perform, entertain

    create, design, present

18. Which is not a medium of communication?

    newspaper

    syllable

    the Internet

19. Which genre of book is this?

    biography

    autobiography

    science fiction

20. Which fashion word is an accessory?

    wristwatch

    wardrobe

    gown

Nature, Fire, and Sport Words

B. Match the nature and fire words with their definitions. Then write "Nature" or "Fire" to label each group.

Nature and Fire Words

| glacial | extinguish | ignite | boulder |
| crackle | brook | flammable | landscape |

_____ Word

_____	_____
to put out fire	burnable
_____	_____
sound of a fire	to start a fire

_____ Word

_____	_____
a huge rock	icy
_____	_____
a small stream	all the visible features of an area

C. Unscramble the sport words and fill in the blanks.

1. The winning soccer team scored a last minute _____ .
    aglo

2. He was just a _____ when he was spotted for his talent.
    riokoe

3. Eva is very flexible so she wants to learn _____ .
    mnsycgaits

4. Alan was selected as the _____ for his hockey team.
    efnesmnade

5. During her first cycling race, Maria broke all previous _____ .
    sdeorcr

6. Ezra's family booked _____ lessons at the resort in the mountains.
    gnisik

7. Ali was excited to practise _____ using his new racket.
    sinetn

Disaster, Astronomy, and Feeling Words

D. Match the disaster, astronomy, and feeling words with their definitions.

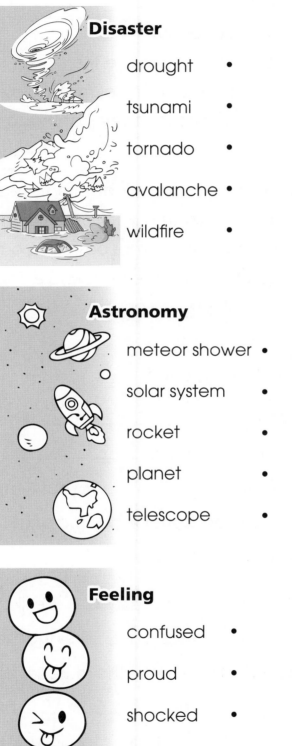

Disaster

drought •

tsunami •

tornado •

avalanche •

wildfire •

- a raging fire in a forested area
- a violent windstorm
- large masses of snow, ice, and rock falling down mountainsides
- lack of rainfall for a prolonged period of time
- enormous waves resulting from an earthquake at the seabed

Astronomy

meteor shower •

solar system •

rocket •

planet •

telescope •

- a human-made device used to view distant objects in the night sky
- countless shooting stars
- the collection of planets with their moons orbiting the sun
- a self-propelling device that can be launched into space
- a celestial body that orbits the sun

Feeling

confused •

proud •

shocked •

distressed •

ashamed •

The way you feel when...

- you win
- you do not understand something
- you are caught doing something wrong
- you lose something
- you receive a nasty surprise

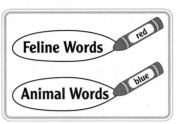

Feline Words — red
Animal Words — blue

Feline, Animal, Medical, and Archaeology Words

E.   Circle the words with the specified colours.

I saw and learned a lot about some of my favourite animals at the Toronto Zoo last Friday. Our class started by visiting the tiger, cheetah, and cougar. Then we went to see the lynx and the leopard. All these members of the cat family reminded me of my Siamese cat, Elise. She loves to purr and chatter on my lap, but the felines at the zoo were kind of scary for me.

After leaving the cat family, Mrs. Lee took us to see some near threatened animals including the beluga and the narwhal. We also read about the giant tortoise, which is categorized as a vulnerable animal. There were posters about endangered animals at the zoo. They showed pictures of the blue whale and the chimpanzee. I wish I could play my part in saving these animals in peril.

F.   Fill in the blanks with the correct medical or archaeology words.

Medical Word

cough

flu

symptoms

runny nose

medicine

Archaeology Word

archaeologist

civilizations

artifacts

excavated

historical

My mother is a doctor. When I have 1._____ like a 2._____ , a sore throat, and a 3._____ , she will give me some 4._____ to cure my 5._____ . I usually feel better in no time at all. I love my mom!

I also love my dad. He is an 6._____ . He likes showing me pictures of the 7._____ sites that he 8._____ . He often takes me to the museum he works at to teach me about ancient 9._____ by studying the 10._____ on display.

I think my parents have very interesting careers and I want to grow up to be just like them!

G. Unscramble the communication words to complete the crossword puzzle.

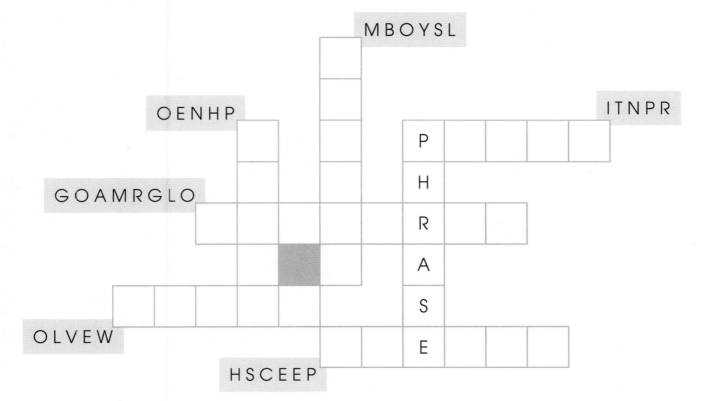

MBOYSL

OENHP

ITNPR

P
H
R
A
S
E

GOAMRGLO

OLVEW

HSCEEP

H. Write the genre and fashion words for the pictures.

Which genres do these characters belong to?

Genre

detective _____

fairy _____

ghost _____

alien _____

What is another word for each fashion word below?

Fashion

handbag _____

pants _____

clothing _____

cloth _____

Section 4

Reading and Writing

UNIT 1

Fortune Telling Newspaper

Cast of Characters

Jake: an 11-year-old paper boy

Mr. Yee: Jake's neighbour

Mike: a resident of the neighbourhood

Mayor (of the city)

ACT 1

Scene 1

SETTING: The story begins on a busy street in the suburbs as Jake begins his paper route.

JAKE: (approaches a neighbour) Good morning, Mr. Yee. Here's your paper.

MR. YEE: Thanks. Oh, look. It says, SUMMER'S HERE TO STAY. It's about time.

JAKE: (looks back and notices Mr. Yee's shirt that says, WELCOME BACK SUMMER) Uh, yeah. (speaking to himself) That was weird. It was like the headline on the newspaper I delivered came true. Here's an ad for MIKE'S MOWING. Let's see what happens. (drops the paper at the next house)

MIKE: (pushes a lawnmower from the side of the house) Hey, Jake!

JAKE: (stares with his mouth open and waves at Mike) I can't believe it! Is it a coincidence? This headline says MAYOR TO RUN AGAIN, and the mayor's house is coming up. Maybe he will run to thank me and give me a big tip! (drops the paper and waits) I guess I was wrong. But maybe if I ring the doorbell…(rings the doorbell)

MAYOR: Hello? Oh, the paper! (takes the paper, pleased to see the headline) Thanks!

JAKE: Enjoy your paper, sir. (walks away, disappointed) It was all a coincidence. I guess I don't have to worry about this GARBAGE STRIKE headline.

(A truck with a wobbly load of garbage turns a sharp corner toward Jake. The mayor sees what is about to happen and breaks into a run.)

MAYOR: Jake! Look out!

A. Circle the answers.

1. How old is Jake?

   ten years old

   eleven years old

   twelve years old

2. Whom does Jake meet first?

   Mike

   Mr. Yee

   the mayor

3. What is written on Mr. Yee's shirt?

   SUMMER'S HERE TO STAY

   WELCOME BACK SUMMER

   MAYOR TO RUN AGAIN

4. What is coming toward Jake?

   a newspaper delivery

   a mowing truck

   a garbage truck

B. Answer the questions.

1. Circle the text form of "Fortune Telling Newspaper".

   newspaper / play / comic

2. What seems "weird" to Jake when he meets Mr. Yee?

   _____

   _____

3. What does Jake think is a "coincidence" when he meets the mayor?

   _____

   _____

4. What do you think is going to happen as the garbage truck heads toward Jake?

   _____

   _____

C.   Read "Fortune Telling Newspaper" again and check the features of a play.

Features of a Play:

1	cast of characters	2	dialogue	3	chapter numbers
4	speech bubbles	5	title	6	setting description
7	author's note	8	monologue	9	stage directions
10	legend	11	props	12	act and scene designations

D.   Write what happens after the mayor runs after Jake to complete the scene. Put your own stage directions in parentheses.

Stage directions are written in the present tense and tell the actors how they must move or speak in a play.

MAYOR: Jake! Look out!

(_____)

JAKE: Thank you, Mr. Mayor. I thought I was done for!

(_____)

If you haven't run after me, I may be tomorrow's headline!

MAYOR: (_____)

No problem, Jake. I might just run for office again, too. (exits)

JAKE: (_____)

_____

(_____)

End of Scene

E. **Write a scene of a play with two characters.**

Topic Ideas:

- exploring a haunted house
- a strange bus ride
- a trip to the museum
- studying for a test

_____
Title

Cast of Characters

_____ : _____

_____ : _____

ACT I
Scene 1

SETTING: _____

_____ : _____
(character)
_____

_____

_____ : _____

_____

_____

_____ : _____

_____

_____

End of Scene

Words that I Have Learned

_____

_____

_____

UNIT 2 The Myth of Daedalus and Icarus

A long time ago, there lived a talented inventor named Daedalus. He could build a great many things and was well-known for his ingenious capabilities.

Upon arriving on the island of Crete, Daedalus befriended King Minos, who ruled the island. King Minos asked him to build a maze, called the Labyrinth, to contain a Minotaur, a terrible creature that was half human and half bull. The Minotaur demanded human sacrifices, and every nine years King Minos would send seven men into the Labyrinth to appease the creature.

One year, among those being sacrificed was the heroic prince of Athens, Theseus. But King Minos's daughter, Ariadne, was in love with him and asked Daedalus to help save him from his fate. With Daedalus's help, Theseus managed to escape the Labyrinth and flee Crete with Ariadne.

King Minos was enraged. As punishment for his betrayal, he locked Daedalus and his son, Icarus, inside the Labyrinth. Daedalus made a plan to escape by air. He used string, feathers, and wax to successfully build large wings for himself and his son.

Before they flew off, he warned his son that he needed to fly at a safe height. If he flew too low, the sea water would dampen his wings and make him sink, and if he flew too high, the sun would melt the wax.

When they finally flew, people below looked up in astonishment at the sight of ordinary men achieving what only gods could. Icarus, feeling vain, forgot his father's warnings and began soaring higher and higher into the sky.

Icarus flew too close to the sun, and sure enough, the wax of his wings began to melt and he plummeted to the sea. Daedalus tried to save him but it was too late. Icarus drowned, leaving behind only the feathers of his wings floating on the water's surface.

Daedalus, in his grief, named the part of the ocean where Icarus fell the "Icarian Sea".

A. Circle the answers.

1. Who is Theseus?

   the prince of Crete

   the prince of Icaria

   the prince of Athens

2. Whom does Ariadne ask to save Theseus?

   Daedalus

   Icarus

   King Minos

3. What does Daedalus use to build the large wings?

   string, feathers, and wax

   string, cloth, and wax

   string, leaves, and wax

4. How does Icarus feel when he flies?

   frightened

   worried

   vain

B. Answer the questions.

1. What is the purpose of this myth?

   _____

   _____

   _____

A myth is a traditional story passed down through history. Myths may explain natural and social phenomena, set social and moral standards, and give reasons for social customs.

2. What is the Labyrinth?

   _____

   _____

3. What does Daedalus warn Icarus will happen if he flies too high in the sky?

   _____

   _____

4. What do you think is the lesson of this myth?

   _____

   _____

Section
4

Reading and Writing

A myth may have these features:

- set in the past
- explains a phenomenon
- explains a social custom
- involves gods, goddesses, heroes, mortals, and magical creatures

- passed through generations
- teaches a moral lesson
- sets a social or moral standard
- contains supernatural events

C. Read the plot and write the myth in your own words.

Title: Pandora's Box

Characters: Pandora (the first woman on earth), Prometheus and Epimetheus (brothers), Zeus (king of the Greek gods)

Plot:

- Prometheus stole fire from heaven.
- Zeus punished him by tricking his brother, Epimetheus, and his wife, Pandora.
- Pandora was given a container and told not to open it.
- She opened it out of curiosity and released all the evil it contained into this world.

Pandora's Box

_____

_____

_____

_____

_____

_____

_____

D. Write a myth using as many features as possible. Then draw a picture to go with it.

My Myth

Title

_____

_____

_____

_____

_____

_____

_____

_____

_____

_____

_____

_____

_____

_____

Words that I Have Learned

_____

_____

_____

UNIT 3 Aladdin

Once upon a time, there was a young boy named Aladdin. His mother spun cotton all day to afford food and clothes for the two of them, but it was not enough. Aladdin knew he needed to earn a living.

One day, a rich tradesman approached Aladdin with an enchanting magic ring. He convinced Aladdin to journey into a dark cave to retrieve a magic oil lamp for him, and told him that no harm would come to him if he wore the ring. Little did Aladdin know that this strange tradesman was actually a wicked sorcerer!

Upon finding the magic oil lamp, Aladdin became entrapped in the dark cave. As he sat in despair, he rubbed the fateful ring against his skin. Miraculously, a genie appeared and asked, "What is your heart's desire?"

Aladdin told the genie he wanted to be set free, and in an instant, he was home with the magic oil lamp at his side. When he rubbed the lamp, another more powerful genie appeared and granted all of Aladdin's wishes. In time, Aladdin became prosperous and caught the attention of the princess, whom he married and lived happily with in a beautiful palace.

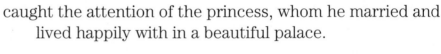

But the sorcerer, envious of Aladdin's fortune, came up with a plan to trick the princess into selling him the lamp. He dressed up as a poor lamp seller trading used, worn-out lamps for shiny, new ones. The princess, who did not know about the real value of the magic lamp, gave him the lamp with the genie. Once the sorcerer had the lamp, he took away Aladdin's palace, riches, and the princess. Aladdin, in grief, once more called on the genie from the magic ring to aid him. He tricked the sorcerer into a deep sleep and took the lamp back. The genie reunited him with the princess and they went home to a restored palace.

Aladdin and his princess lived there in happiness, enjoying their good fortune, and the wicked sorcerer was never heard from again.

A. Circle the answers.

1. What does Aladdin's mother do?

   makes bread

   spins cotton

   sells fruits

3. Who is Aladdin's employer?

   a witch

   a princess

   a sorcerer

2. Aladdin tries to find work because
   _____ .

   he is poor

   he is bored

   he is told to

4. How many genies are there?

   one

   two

   three

B. Answer the questions.

1. Why do you think Aladdin agrees to work for the tradesman?

   _____

   _____

   _____

2. How does Aladdin get out of the cave?

   _____

   _____

3. Explain the main problem and solution in this folk tale.

   _____

   _____

   _____

   _____

A folk tale is a story that has been passed down by word of mouth from generation to generation.

C. **Read the folk tale again. Then fill in the information.**

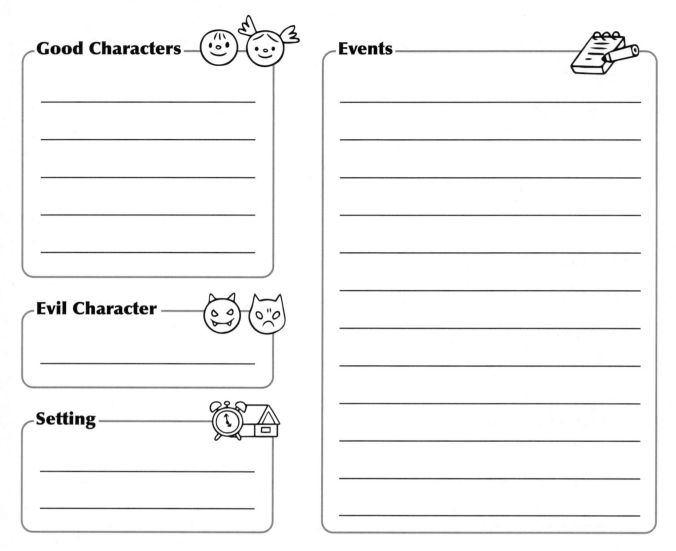

Good Characters

Events

Evil Character

Setting

D. **Check the boxes to show the characteristics of the folk tale "Aladdin".**

The Characteristics of the Folk Tale "Aladdin":

☐ passed down through generations

☐ begins with "Once upon a time" or "Long ago"

☐ contains a problem and solution

☐ contains facts

☐ has a happy ending

☐ evil is punished

☐ has diagrams

☐ includes magical elements

E. Create a short folk tale of your own. Check the characteristics that your folk tale contains.

┌─ **Title** ─────────────────────────┐
│   │
└─────────────────────────────────────┘

My Folk Tale Checklist

○ begins with "Once upon a time" or "Long ago"

○ good characters

○ evil characters

○ magical elements

○ problem and solution

○ happy ending

_____

_____

_____

_____

_____

_____

_____

_____

_____

_____

_____

_____

_____

_____

_____

Words that I Have Learned

_____

_____

_____

Power for Sale

Once upon a time, in the realm of gnomes and fairies, there were two small gnomes who were always cooking up ways to make easy money, but all they seemed to cause was mischief.

It was April Fool's Day and the gnomes had an idea to make money again. When a fairy named Frieda flew by with her heavy head and her tired wings, the gnomes sprung into action. "Power for sale! Power for sale!" they called out. Frieda's ears perked up. "This is just what I need," she thought. Lately, she had not been sleeping well. The gnomes convinced her that by keeping their special pebble in her pocket, she would have power and energy. So, Frieda bought the little grey pebble, and the gleeful gnomes pocketed Frieda's five dollars.

Soon, word spread to other fairies, and the gnomes sold two more pebbles: one that promised luck and one that guaranteed courage. Fifteen dollars better off now, the gnomes saw an opportunity: they could open a store and sell pebbles that give things like talent, beauty, and hope. They would be rich!

But then something happened and brought the gnomes back to reality. Frieda lost her pebble! Before she knew it was lost, though, she walked around with as much energy as she had when it was safe in her pocket. She realized that she did not derive the power from the tiny pebble after all. It must have come from the sleep she was finally getting! Feeling foolish, Frieda went to her fairy friends. Together, they tramped up to the gnomes. "The pebble you sold me doesn't give luck!" said one fairy. "This pebble doesn't give courage at all!" another fairy complained.

The gnomes realized their mistakes. So they put down their pebbles and picked up their paintbrushes – to make magnificent paintings. Once again, word spread about the gnomes' business, but this time, it was about their beautiful paintings. The gnomes worked hard and they were surprised to find how much money and how many friends they could make without tricking anyone!

The gnomes and the fairies all lived together in the realm happily ever after.

A. Circle the answers.

1. How many gnomes are there?

   one

   two

   three

2. What verb tense is used?

   past

   present

   future

3. What do the pebbles promise?

   hope, beauty, and power

   success, luck, and warmth

   comfort, prestige, and beauty

4. What do the gnomes sell at the end?

   pebbles

   paints

   paintings

Power for sale!

$5.⁰⁰ each

B. Answer the questions.

1. What text form is "Power for Sale"?

   _____

   _____

2. What mischievous idea do the gnomes come up with?

   _____

   _____

3. What makes Frieda realize that she has been tricked?

   _____

   _____

4. What do the gnomes do to mend their mischief?

   _____

   _____

Section 4

Reading and Writing

Like many folk tales, a fairy tale is a story that has a good character (hero), a bad character (villain), magical elements, and a happy ending. It usually begins with "Once upon a time" and ends with "lived happily ever after".

C.   Write about the characteristics of "Power for Sale".

Title: _____

Characters

Hero:

Villain:

Problem

Setting

Time:

Place:

Solution

Events

_____

_____

_____

_____

_____

_____

_____

D. Create a fairy tale of your own. Then draw the characters in your story.

Title

_____

_____

_____

_____

_____

_____

_____

_____

_____

_____

_____

_____

_____

_____

_____

Hero

Villain

Words that I Have Learned

_____

_____

_____

UNIT
5 Summer List

It's almost September.
I can count on one fist
The great things I did
From my summer list.

At the park, by a sea of flowers,
I swung on the swing.
But a grumpy bee was annoyed
And I got a sting.

I thought my new rod
Would give me my wish.
But it slipped from my hands
Now it swims happily with the fish.

Then the fair came to town
With lots of new stuff.
Like exciting rides! But I
Was not tall enough.

There's one more thing
On my list, I see.
It says, this summer
To climb a tall tree.

I'll do it! I'm sure
That I won't fall.
Here's a good tree
It's sturdy. It's tall.

I hoist myself up
And as I grow taller,
The world beneath me
Gets smaller and smaller.

I can't stop here;
It's the climb of all climbs.
I can't let this end
Like all those other times.

I look up again;
I see only one big sky.
There's nowhere to go
Unless I fly.

I've reached the top!
I'm at the crown!
Now...how on earth
Will I get down?

A. Circle the answers.

1. What is the poem about?

   summer activities

   the summer fair

   a tall tree

2. Where does the writer swing on the swing?

   near the tree

   at school

   at the park

3. What swims with the fish?

   the flowers

   the crown

   the fishing rod

4. What is at the fair?

   a tall, sturdy tree

   rides

   a bee

B. Answer the questions.

1. Write four rhyming pairs from the poem.

   _____

   _____

2. Give examples of imagery used in the poem.

   _____

   _____

   _____

   _____

 Imagery is the use of descriptive language to create vivid pictures in the reader's mind.

3. What four problems does the writer have during the summer?

   _____

   _____

   _____

   _____

C.   Read the poem.   Then answer the questions.

Fall

Fall,
Is my favourite season of all!

I roll up my sleeves,
And jump on the colourful blanket of leaves.

My sister and I,
Make carefree kites to fly.

We dress up for Halloween,
This year I was a queen!

We visit the pumpkin farm,
And run around arm in arm.

Fall is lots of fun,
For us to enjoy the last bit of sun.

We have leaves to rake,
And warm apple pies to bake.

That is why fall,
Is the best season of all!

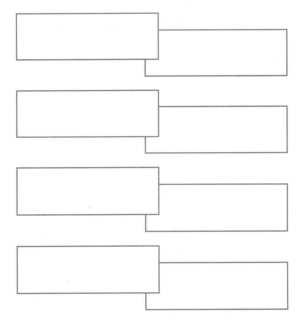

1.   Check the characteristics of this poem.

○   written in stanzas

○   shows the poet's feelings

○   contains imagery

○   contains rhyming words

○   tells a story

○   does not rhyme

2.   List the rhyming pairs.

3.   Write two examples of imagery from the poem.

_____

_____

_____

D. Write a poem about your favourite season. Use imagery and rhyming pairs. Then draw a picture to go with your poem.

My Poem

Title: _____

_____

_____

_____

_____

_____

_____

_____

_____

_____

_____

_____

_____

_____

_____

Words that I Have Learned

_____

_____

_____

Reading and Writing

Marilyn Bell

Marilyn Bell –
Marathon Swimmer

By Eugene Griffin

Braving Lake Ontario

On September 8, 1954, a few brave swimmers stepped into the chilly, 21°C Lake Ontario water at Youngstown, New York. Marilyn Bell was swimming for Canada and the much-anticipated race was on!

It did not take long for Marilyn Bell to show her strength. Five kilometres from the American shore, she had overtaken Chadwick, and by 6:00 a.m., Chadwick had been pulled from the water after 26 km. Leuszler quit at the 32-km mark, leaving Bell as the only competitor.

Harsh Swimming Conditions

The swimming conditions were less than ideal. It rained through the night and the water temperature dropped to 16°C. The water was choppy but Bell managed to maintain a steady 60 strokes a minute, at a pace of almost three kilometres per hour. Her biggest difficulty was boredom. On more than one occasion, Bell fell asleep and her

coach, Gus Ryder, had to wake her up. She was fed baby food and syrup on a stick alongside the boat.

Our National Treasure

On the Canadian side, the radio stations had been broadcasting her progress and thousands of extra newspapers were being printed to meet the public demand for this incredible story. When she completed the 52.5-km swim and sat in the ambulance recovering, she exclaimed that she felt terrific. The CNE gave Bell the prize money and she received another $50 000 worth of gifts. She became an instant celebrity and a national treasure.

Marilyn Bell before her feat of swimming in Lake Ontario

Sports Exclusive

67

A. Circle the answers.

1. Where did the swimming race take place?

   in Lake Erie

   in Lake Ontario

   at CNE

2. When did Chadwick quit?

   by 6:00 p.m.

   by 6:00 a.m.

   by 7:00 a.m.

3. Who was Bell's coach?

   Gus Ryder

   Chadwick

   Leuszler

4. How was Bell's progress broadcast?

   through magazines

   through radio stations

   through articles

5. How did Bell feel upon completing the swim?

   terrified

   bored

   terrific

B. Answer the questions.

1. Circle the text form of "Marilyn Bell – Marathon Swimmer".

   autobiography / magazine article / fable

2. What were some of the challenges faced by Bell?

   _____

   _____

   _____

3. How was Bell rewarded for completing the swim?

   _____

   _____

   _____

Section 4

Reading and Writing

A magazine is an informational text that shares facts and information on certain topics. It aims to inform and entertain. It consists of many articles that are mostly based on facts but are written from the writer's perspective.

C. Fill in or circle the information about the article.

These are some features of a magazine article.

Name of Magazine: _____

Type of Magazine: **travel / literary / sports**

Headline of Article: _____

Byline: _____

Subheadings: _____

_____

_____

Images: **cartoons / photos / graphics**

Caption: _____

_____

Purpose: to **inform / instruct / persuade / entertain**

Target Audience: _____

_____

Other Features: _____

_____

_____

_____

D. Create a magazine article of your own. Then draw a picture and add a caption to go with it.

Topic Ideas:
- sports
- food
- travel
- pet
- fashion
- science

Headline _____

Byline _____

_____   _____
_____   _____
_____   _____
_____   _____
_____   _____
_____   _____
_____   _____
_____
_____
_____   Caption
_____

Words that I Have Learned

_____
_____
_____

UNIT
7

The History of the Canadian Flag

Look at the timeline to learn the history of our flag!

Year   Event

1497
The first Canadian flag was likely the St. George's Cross, a 15th century English flag. John Cabot reached the east coast of Canada in 1497 and erected the flag, claiming the land for England.

St. George's Cross

1534
Jacques Cartier hoisted the fleur-de-lis, firmly establishing French sovereignty in Canada.

Fleur-de-lis

1760s
In the early 1760s, Canada was ceded to the United Kingdom and the Royal Union flag, more commonly known as the Union Jack, became the official flag of Canada.

Union Jack

1945
The Red Ensign flag, a cross between the Union Jack and a shield bearing the arms of Nova Scotia, Ontario, New Brunswick, and Quebec, originated as a Merchant Marine flag in 1707. The British admiralty accepted the Red Ensign as the official Canadian maritime flag. In 1924, the Order of Council replaced the original shield on the Red Ensign with the Canadian Coat of Arms. In 1945, it was declared the interim flag of Canada.

Canadian Ensign

1965
The Canadian Ensign was replaced by the current red and white maple leaf flag that is the proud symbol of Canada today.

Canadian Flag

A. Circle the answers.

1. Who erected the first flag?

   Jacques Cartier

   John Cabot

   the Order of Council

2. How are the events arranged?

   in chronological order

   in alphabetical order

   in random order

3. Which flag established French sovereignty?

   the Red Ensign

   the St. George's Cross

   the Fleur-de-lis

4. When was the Canadian flag finalized?

   in 1760

   in 1945

   in 1965

B. Answer the questions.

1. What list of events does the timeline show?

   _____

   _____

   _____

A timeline is a graphic line that shows a list of events in chronological order.

2. Write 1 to 5 to list the flags in chronological order.

   ◯ the Canadian Ensign

   ◯ the Union Jack

   ◯ the Fleur-de-lis

   ◯ the St. George's Cross

   ◯ the Canadian Flag

3.

   Describe the Red Ensign flag.

   _____

   _____

   _____

   _____

C. Research and fill in the information.

Prime Ministers of Canada

Write the names of the first five prime ministers of Canada and record the dates they took office. Then write one major event that happened in Canada while they were in office.

You can search for information online or in a book.

Prime Minister (date)	Major Event
1.	
2.	
3.	
4.	
5.	

D. Create a timeline using the information from (C).

Prime Ministers of Canada

Date Taking
Office

Prime Minister and Major Event

_____

_____

_____

_____

_____

_____

_____

_____

_____

_____

_____

_____

_____

_____

_____

Words that I Have Learned

_____

_____

_____

Think Big!

A mural is a large scale piece of art on a wall, ground, or ceiling. One of the most famous murals was painted on the ceiling of the Sistine Chapel in Italy. It is called *The Creation of Adam*. Although *The Creation of Adam* was complicated to complete, you can make a simple mural of your own with the help of your parents or friends, some basic materials, and step-by-step instructions!

How to Make Your Own Ground Mural

Steps:

1. Draw or trace an image you would like to turn into a mural on a transparency sheet with a transparency marker and set aside.

Materials Needed:

- transparency sheet
- transparency marker
- sidewalk chalk

2. On a sunny day, go outside with your parent or a friend. Have your helper hold the transparency sheet with the image you drew high up so that the image is projected onto the ground.

3. Draw the outline of the projected image on the ground with the sidewalk chalk.

4. Colour your big ground mural with the sidewalk chalk.

5. Invite your friends and family to see your new creation.

A. Circle the answers.

1. What is *The Creation of Adam*?

   a famous artist

   a famous chapel

   a famous mural

2. Where was *The Creation of Adam* painted?

   on a wall

   on a floor

   on a ceiling

3. What does "complicated" in the introduction mean?

   easy

   difficult

   boring

4. What is Step 4 about?

   colouring the mural

   drawing the mural

   projecting the image

B. Answer the questions.

1. What text form is "Think Big!"?

   _____

2. What is the purpose of this text form?

   _____

   _____

3. Check the characteristics of this text form.

   ◯ numbers to show order

   ◯ simple and clear language

   ◯ descriptive language

   ◯ imperative sentences

   ◯ step-by-step instructions

   ◯ helpful illustrations

   ◯ charts

   ◯ list

   ◯ heading

   ◯ subheadings

   ◯ labels

   ◯ graphs

C.   Think about one thing you would like to make by yourself. Brainstorm ideas for the instructions that you will write using the mind map.

Mind Map

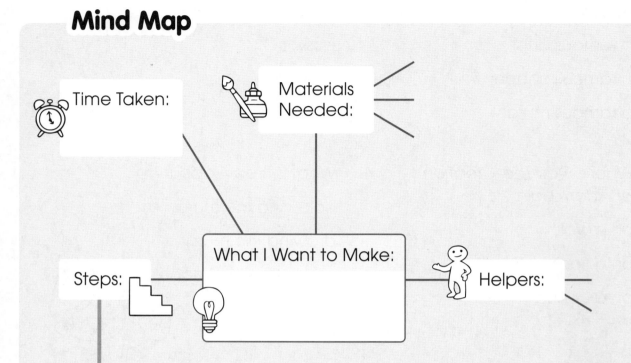

Time Taken:

Materials Needed:

What I Want to Make:

Steps:

Helpers:

D. Write step-by-step instructions for the thing that you would like to make using your ideas from (C). Then draw to show what it is.

Title: _____

Time Taken: _____

Steps:

_____

_____

What I Will Make

_____

_____

_____

_____

_____

_____

_____

_____

_____

_____

Materials Needed

•

•

•

Words that I Have Learned

_____

_____

_____

UNIT
9 The Amazing Helen Keller

Helen Keller's Milestones and Achievements

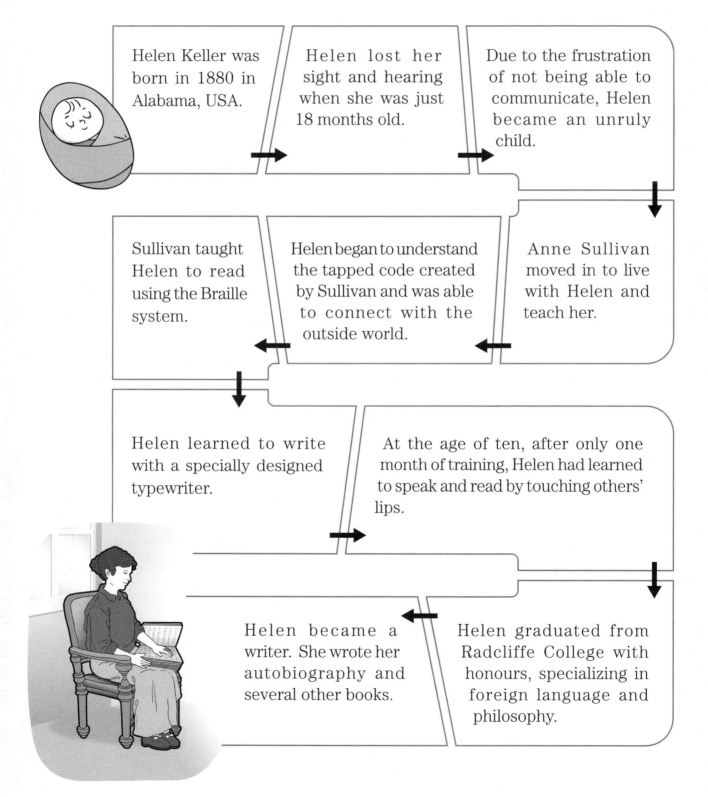

Helen Keller was born in 1880 in Alabama, USA.

Helen lost her sight and hearing when she was just 18 months old.

Due to the frustration of not being able to communicate, Helen became an unruly child.

Sullivan taught Helen to read using the Braille system.

Helen began to understand the tapped code created by Sullivan and was able to connect with the outside world.

Anne Sullivan moved in to live with Helen and teach her.

Helen learned to write with a specially designed typewriter.

At the age of ten, after only one month of training, Helen had learned to speak and read by touching others' lips.

Helen became a writer. She wrote her autobiography and several other books.

Helen graduated from Radcliffe College with honours, specializing in foreign language and philosophy.

A. Circle the answers.

1. When was Helen Keller born?

   in 1818

   in 1880

   in 1888

2. Where was she born?

   in Alaska, USA

   in Alabama, USA

   in Alberta, Canada

3. Who was Anne Sullivan?

   a doctor

   a nanny

   a teacher

4. What was one of Helen's specializations in college?

   foreign language

   literature

   English language

B. Answer the questions.

 Graphic organizers are diagrams that help organize ideas and information to show how they are related to one another.

1. Circle the type of graphic organizer of this text.

   Venn diagram / timeline / flow diagram / cycle diagram

2. Why did Helen become an unruly child?

   _____

   _____

3. How did Helen communicate with others at first with Sullivan's help?

   _____

   _____

4. What are Helen's academic achievements?

   _____

   _____

   _____

C. **Look at "The Amazing Helen Keller" again. Fill in or circle the information. Then answer the questions.**

1. Title of the graphic organizer:

   _____

2. Features of the graphic organizer:

   title / subheadings / graphic boxes / legend / arrows /

   caption / labels / pictures

3. In what order are the events arranged?

   _____

4. What are used to show the order of the events?

   _____

5. Why is a timeline not an ideal graphic organizer to present the events?

   _____

D. **Brainstorm and research ideas for a flow diagram about a sequence of events that happened to a person you admire.**

 My Ideas

E. **Create a flow diagram about a sequence of events that happened to a person based on your ideas from (D). Then draw a picture of the person in the circle.**

Title

Words that I Have Learned

THE SUNSHINE NEWS

April 4, 2019

Bigfoot Sighting at Annual Race

By May Flower

There may have been more than the usual tired feet at last weekend's Run for Fun. Over a hundred people participated in the annual run and some of them had an unexpected surprise. Near the finish line, runners reported seeing a huge, furry creature with very large feet.

"I saw it peering at us from behind the bushes," said Barry Fool, owner of The Shoe Fool and sponsor of this year's Run for Fun. "It seemed harmless enough. It seemed a bit shy."

Other runners were skeptical. A runner named Anna said, "Someone was having fun in a big monkey suit. Honestly, his feet were so big he couldn't walk properly."

The police, however, are reacting with caution. Police Chief Melissa Murphy said they are doing a thorough search of the area, and she urges the public to be cautious.

"Keep your children and pets inside," said Murphy. "At least until we get this sorted out."

A huge, furry creature was reported near the finish line.

The police are also asking the public to contact them if they have any information or pictures of the mysterious creature.

Run for Fun organizers said this is the first time Bigfoot has been spotted during the race. Run for Fun has been a favourite annual event for over 20 years in this town, and is always held on April 1.

When asked about the future of the race, Fool said there was no reason it would not go on next year with even more participants. "I think people have an even better reason to run now," said Fool.

A. Circle the answers.

1. What is the annual run called?

   Sun and Fun

   Fun in the Sun

   Run for Fun

2. When did the sighting take place?

   on a weekday

   on April 1, 2019

   on April 4, 2019

3. Where was the creature seen?

   behind the bushes

   at a zoo

   in a shoe shop

4. Who is Barry Fool?

   the owner of Run for Fun

   the owner of The Shoe Fool

   the sponsor of The Shoe Fool

B. Answer the questions.

1. What text form is "Bigfoot Sighting"?

   _____

2. Is this text fiction or non-fiction? Why?

   _____

   _____

3. What is the purpose of the text?

   _____

4. What was the unexpected surprise for some participants?

   _____

   _____

5. Why did Barry Fool say, "I think people have an even better reason to run now"?

   _____

   _____

C.   Read "Bigfoot Sighting" again. Then fill in the information.

These are the features of a newspaper article.

1.   Name of Newspaper: _____

2.   Date: _____

3.   Headline: _____

4.   Byline: _____

5.   Introduction: Paragraph _____

6.   Body: Paragraphs _____

7.   Photo Caption: _____

8.   Examples of Quotes:

By Anna: _____

_____

By Murphy: _____

_____

D.   Brainstorm ideas for a newspaper article that you will write.

Answer the questions:

• Who?   _____

• What?   _____

• When?   _____

• Where?   _____

• Why?   _____

• How?   _____

E. Write a newspaper article using your ideas from (D). Then draw a photo and add a caption to go with the article.

NEWS

_____ , _____

_____
Title

By _____

_____

_____

_____

_____

_____   _____

_____   _____

_____   _____

_____   _____

_____   _____

_____   _____

Words that I Have Learned

_____

_____

_____

UNIT

11 The Volcano

volcano

volcano – A volcano is a mountain with an opening through which lava, ash, gases, and rock fragments have erupted from below the Earth's surface.

Formation

Volcanoes are made of layers of molten rock erupting from the Earth's surface. The hot fluid lava spreads over a wide area. Over time, the added layers form the shape of the mountain.

Types

There are different types of volcanoes. Some are active, such as Mount St. Helens in the United States. Others are dormant, such as Mount Edziza in Canada.

Structure of a Volcano

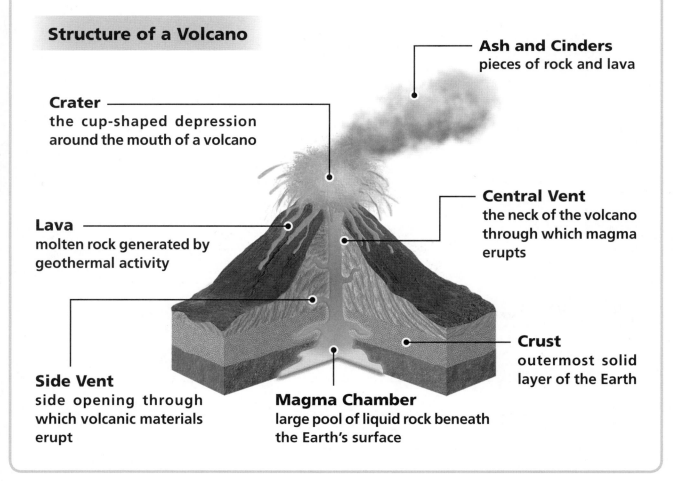

Ash and Cinders
pieces of rock and lava

Crater
the cup-shaped depression
around the mouth of a volcano

Lava
molten rock generated by
geothermal activity

Central Vent
the neck of the volcano
through which magma
erupts

Side Vent
side opening through
which volcanic materials
erupt

Magma Chamber
large pool of liquid rock beneath
the Earth's surface

Crust
outermost solid
layer of the Earth

A. Circle the answers.

1. What is the outermost layer of the Earth called?

   vent

   chamber

   crust

3. What is lava made of?

   molten ash

   molten gas

   molten rock

2. Where is the crater of a volcano?

   around the mouth

   on the side

   beneath the Earth's surface

4. What generates lava?

   geothermal activity

   solar activity

   wind activity

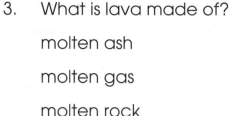

B. Answer the questions.

1. Circle the text form of "The Volcano".

   newspaper article / encyclopedia entry / history book entry

2. Name the features of this text form.

   _____

3. How is the volcano formed?

   _____

   _____

4. Research and write the definitions of "active" and "dormant" volcanoes. Then give one more example of each.

active volcano

_____

Definition

_____

_____

Example

dormant volcano

_____

Definition

_____

_____

Example

C.   Read "The Volcano" again. Then fill in the information and answer the questions.

1.   Entry: _____

2.   Subheadings: _____

3.   Diagram Title: _____

4.   Labels: _____

_____

5.

> *Where do you think this entry is in the encyclopedia: near the beginning, middle, or end of the book? Why?*

_____

_____

D.   Brainstorm and research ideas for another encyclopedia entry about one of the given topics.

My Ideas

ocean

mountain

river

desert

forest

E. **Create an encyclopedia entry using your ideas from (D). Include a diagram with a title and labels.**

_____
Entry

_____
Title of Diagram

Words that I Have Learned

_____

_____

_____

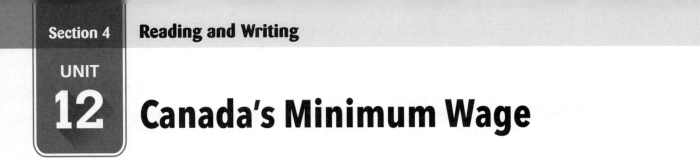

The minimum wage is the lowest wage permitted by law that an employer can pay an employee. The given map shows the minimum wage by province across Canada in the year 2018.

Canada's Hourly Minimum Wage by Province

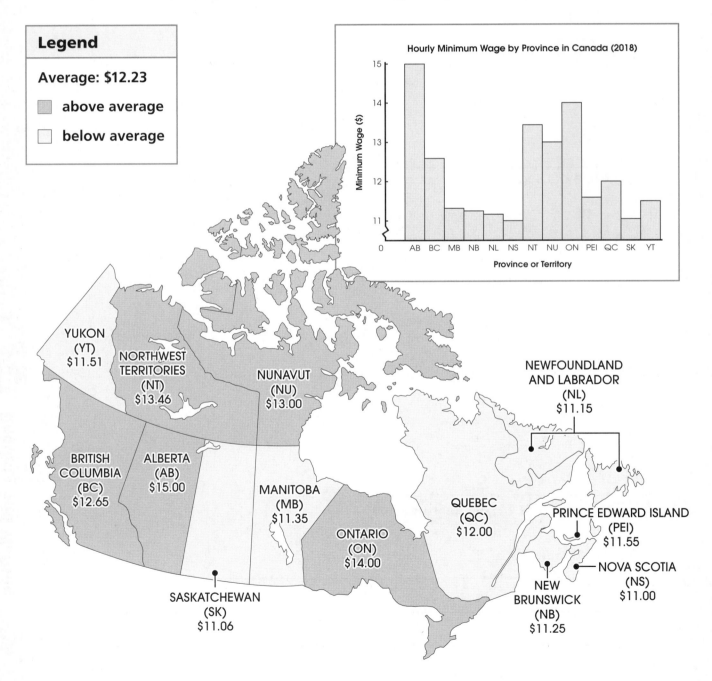

Legend

Average: **$12.23**

⬜ above average

☐ below average

Hourly Minimum Wage by Province in Canada (2018)

Minimum Wage ($)

AB BC MB NB NL NS NT NU ON PEI QC SK YT

Province or Territory

YUKON
(YT)
$11.51

NORTHWEST
TERRITORIES
(NT)
$13.46

NUNAVUT
(NU)
$13.00

NEWFOUNDLAND
AND LABRADOR
(NL)
$11.15

BRITISH
COLUMBIA
(BC)
$12.65

ALBERTA
(AB)
$15.00

MANITOBA
(MB)
$11.35

ONTARIO
(ON)
$14.00

QUEBEC
(QC)
$12.00

PRINCE EDWARD ISLAND
(PEI)
$11.55

NOVA SCOTIA
(NS)
$11.00

NEW
BRUNSWICK
(NB)
$11.25

SASKATCHEWAN
(SK)
$11.06

A. Circle the answers.

1. Which province has the highest minimum wage?

   Alberta

   Manitoba

   Ontario

2. What does the legend show?

   names of places

   range of minimum wage

   average minimum wage

3. Which provinces have a below average minimum wage?

   SK and AB

   ON and NB

   NS and PEI

4. What is the lowest minimum wage in Canada?

   $11.00

   $10.96

   $10.85

B. Answer the questions.

1. What is the title of the map?

   _____

2. What is the title of the graph?

   _____

3. Which province or territory has the lowest minimum wage?

   _____

4. What is the range of minimum wage in Canada?

   $_____ to $_____

5. Which elements give you more information, the graphic elements or the text? Explain.

   _____

   _____

   _____

Section
4

Reading and Writing

C. **Use the information provided to colour the map and answer the questions.**

Canadian Atlas   p. 15

Hourly Minimum
Wage in Canada

	Apr 2017	Apr 2018
AB	$12.20	$13.60
BC	$10.85	$11.35
MB	$11	$11.15
NB	$11	$11.25
NL	$10.75	$11.15
NS	$10.85	$11
NT	$12.50	$13.46
NU	$13	$13
ON	$11.40	$14
PEI	$11.25	$11.55
QC	$10.75	$11.25
SK	$10.72	$10.96
YT	$11.32	$11.51

Source: Stats Canada's Minimum Wage Database

The Change in Hourly Minimum Wage in Canada
(April 2017 – April 2018)

Legend

Provinces/Territories with

blue   increased wage

red   no change in wage

1. Write the information.

   Name of the Book: _____

   Title of the Table: _____

   Title of the Map: _____

2. Describe how each element is used on the map.

   Legend: _____

   Table: _____

   Colours: _____

D. Research to complete the map of Canada's physical regions. Then colour.

Canadian Atlas

_____

Legend

Words that I Have Learned

_____

_____

_____

FILE   MESSAGE   INSERT   OPTIONS   FORMAT   TEXT   PREVIEW

To: cayenne@smart.com   **Cc:**

Subject: I can't play this Saturday!

Send   **Attachments:**

Hi Cayenne,

I hope you are doing great. I was so excited for this Saturday's soccer game but I need to tell you that I won't be able to play anymore.

It's because I sprained my ankle as I ran to save my younger brother from falling off the sofa yesterday! I felt sharp pains down my leg and my parents rushed me to the hospital. They had to support me as I wobbled into the emergency room. After a long wait, a technician took my X-ray. The doctor said I had a sprained ankle and recommended a lot of rest for a few days. I need to go to a few physiotherapy sessions later on. So...now I have to miss our game.

I do have an idea, though! The juniors have been practising hard, so maybe one of them can play in my place. I'm confident that you, as my best friend and team captain, will do your best and encourage everybody to play well even if one of us can't play a game. In the meantime, I'll be watching soccer on TV and taking notes on how to be an even better defender when I join you all again on the field.

I wanna catch up with you after the game so come over and celebrate with me if we win!

Best of luck for the game!

Sincerely,

Melinda

A. Circle the answers.

1. Which sport is mentioned?

   tennis

   badminton

   soccer

2. Which part of Melinda's body was injured?

   her elbow

   her ankle

   her knee

3. Who took Melinda's X-ray?

   a doctor

   a physician

   a technician

4. What position does Melinda play on the team?

   defender

   striker

   goalkeeper

B. Answer the questions.

1. Who is the sender of the e-mail?

   _____

2. Who is the recipient?

   _____

3. Suggest another subject for the e-mail.

   _____

4. How was Melinda hurt?

   _____

   _____

5. What advice did the doctor give?

   _____

   _____

6. Is this e-mail formal or informal? Why?

   _____

   _____

C. Read the e-mail. Then fill in or circle the information.

FILE   MESSAGE   INSERT   OPTIONS   FORMAT   TEXT   PREVIEW

To: melinda@smart.com   **Cc:**

Subject: Get well soon

Send   **Attachments:** 1.jpg   2.jpg   3.jpg

Hi Melinda,

I'm sorry to hear about your injury. I hope you'll get well soon and play soccer again with us – the winners of last night's game!

To make you feel like part of the action, I'm attaching some pictures of our victory and I'll go over to your place in the evening to celebrate.

Let me know if there's anything else I can do to make you feel better.

Sincerely,

Cayenne

1.   Sender: _____   Recipient: _____

2.   Recipient's E-mail Address: _____

3.   Subject: _____

4.   Number of Attachments: _____

     Filenames: _____   _____   _____

5.   Language Used: **formal / informal**

     Examples: • _____

                • _____

                • _____

D. **Imagine you are Melinda. Write a reply to Cayenne's e-mail in (C).**

To:

Cc: Bcc:

Subject:

Attachments:

Words that I Have Learned

_____

_____

_____

UNIT 14 Sunrise Paradise

Sunrise Paradise invites you to stay at our resort and breathe in the fresh sea breeze as you marvel at the panoramic view from our spa windows.

Sunrise Paradise Getaway

Your Home Away from Home!

Activities

Your children can enjoy hours of fun at our magical Trampoline Palace, play water polo in our all-season pool, watch movies in our exclusive theatre, or simply make sandcastles on the tranquil Paradise Beach.

Events

Sunrise Paradise Resort has the perfect venues for hosting birthdays, weddings, and other special events. Let us know how we can make your visit better.

Contact Us

To make your vacation better, we also offer convenient transportation services to and from the airport. You are welcome to stop by our reception desk and request a complimentary guided tour of the area at any time of the day!

Give us a call today to speak to a customer service representative and book your very own resort vacation at Sunrise Paradise! You can also e-mail us for any queries.

Phone: 416-XXX-XXXX

E-mail: paradise@smart.com

Address: 11 Paradise Avenue, Canada

For details, please visit our website.

sunriseparadise.smart.ca

A. Circle the answers.

1. What is the text promoting?

   a product

   a service

   a cause

2. What is Sunrise Paradise?

   a spa

   a beach

   a resort

3. Where is Sunrise Paradise?

   near a forest

   in a palace

   by a beach

4. To whom can customers speak when they call?

   a manager

   a customer service representative

   a receptionist

B. Answer the questions.

1. What is the purpose of the text?

   _____

2. What activities can children do at Sunrise Paradise?

   _____

   _____

3. What events can be hosted at Sunrise Paradise?

   _____

   _____

4. What additional information could be provided for the reader?

   _____

   _____

   _____

A leaflet is a sheet of paper printed on one or both sides to give information about something or to advertise something. It is usually distributed free.

C. **Read "Sunrise Paradise" again. Then check or fill in the information about the features of the leaflet.**

1. Title: _____

2. Slogan: _____

3. Subheadings:

   _____

   _____

   _____

4. Visuals and Graphics:

   ◯ photos   ◯ graphs

   ◯ diagrams   ◯ maps

   ◯ logo   ◯ large bold font

   ◯ lists   ◯ text boxes

5. Language:

   ◯ in the past tense

   ◯ in the present tense

   ◯ in the future tense

   ◯ uses imperatives

   ◯ uses questions

6. Useful Information:

   ◯ company's name

   ◯ company's address

   ◯ contact information

   ◯ room rates

   ◯ cancellation policy

7. Phone Number: _____

   E-mail Address: _____

   Website: _____

D. **Create a leaflet to advertise a product or a service using as many features of a leaflet as possible.**

_____
Title

Contact Us

Words that I Have Learned

_____

_____

_____

Reading and Writing

A. Circle the answers.

1. Which is not a feature of a play?

   cast of characters

   label

   dialogue

2. The purpose of a play is to _____ .

   advertise

   inform

   entertain

3. What text form can be used to teach a moral lesson?

   myth

   instructions

   timeline

4. A story that has been passed down by word of mouth through generations is _____ .

   a fairy tale

   a folk tale

   a poem

5. Which is not a feature of a fairy tale?

   includes good characters (heroes)

   includes bad characters (villains)

   includes factual information

6. Imagery is the use of _____ in a poem.

   fictional characters

   descriptive language

   subheadings

7. What goes with a photo in a magazine article?

   a byline

   a subheading

   a caption

8. Which is not a feature of a magazine article?

   includes a happy ending

   includes subheadings

   includes a variety of fonts

9. A timeline is a form of _____ text.

   informational

   literary

   graphic

Timeline	
Year	Event
	2010 – Birth
	2014 – 1st Day of School
	2019 – Won the soccer tournament

10. A timeline is arranged in _____ .

    chronological order

    alphabetical order

    numerical order

11. What feature is used to provide clear and concise instructions?

    subheadings

    step-by-step instructions

    labels

12. Which one organizes ideas and information to show their connections?

    an e-mail

    a graphic organizer

    a leaflet

13. What are the features of a flow diagram?

    title, caption, and arrows

    title, legend, and arrows

    title, graphic boxes, and arrows

14. What does a byline contain?

    the name of the writer

    the name of the newspaper

    the name of the editor

15. Where is a caption placed in a newspaper article?

    directly above a photo

    directly below a photo

    directly after the headline

16. An encyclopedia entry contains _____ .

    labels, diagrams, and subheadings

    labels, instructions, and diagrams

    labels, maps, and poems

17. What does a legend provide?

    information about a table

    information about a graph

    information about a map

18. What can be used to present factual information?

    myths and instructions

    graphs and maps

    graphs and folk tales

19. _____ can be sent with an e-mail as an attachment.

    The recipient's email address

    The sender's email address

    A picture

20. What can companies use to identify themselves on a leaflet?

    their logo

    activities and events

    customer service representatives

B. Read the text. Then circle "T" for the true statements and "F" for the false ones.

THE SUNSHINE NEWS

July 22, 2018

Man Rescued by *Voyage II*

By Anthony de Luca

The captain and crew of *Voyage II* saved a 30-year-old male from drowning during the early hours of Thursday, July 19 – the second day of the ship's journey.

The captain and crew of *Voyage II* rescuing a passenger

"*Voyage II* was scheduled to visit six Caribbean islands in seven days at sea," says the captain, who hopes to resume the cruise after a thorough examination of the circumstances leading to the situation has been conducted.

"The captain had just announced a warning about dangerous conditions on the wet deck when I heard a commotion on the left side of the ship," reported a crew member.

A man in civilian clothing could be seen flailing his arms in the water as shocked passengers watched helplessly. As the drowning man was not wearing a life jacket, it was apparent that quick action had to be taken.

The captain ordered his crew to carry out an immediate rescue. Fortunately for Mr. Sue, the 30-year-old male who was later identified as a passenger of the luxury cruise ship, the quick thinking of the crew saved his life.

"I was enjoying the beautiful sunrise and before I knew it, I had fallen overboard. I can never thank *Voyage II* enough!" Mr. Sue told our team later.

"It has restored my faith in the cruise line!" beamed Mrs. Sue.

It still remains to be seen whether or not Mr. Sue had heard the captain's warning. However, it has been confirmed that no further accidents occurred on *Voyage II*.

1. The article was written by Anthony Lucas. T / F

2. The incident mentioned in the article happened on the third day of the cruise. T / F

3. The captain warned the passengers of dangerous conditions on the wet deck. T / F

4. Mr. Sue was thirty years old at the time of the incident. T / F

5. Shocked passengers helped save Mr. Sue. T / F

6. The incident took place at dawn. T / F

7. Mr. Sue was happy with the cruise line. T / F

C. Answer the questions.

1. What text form is "Man Rescued by *Voyage II*"?

   _____

2. Read the text again. Then fill in the information.

   • Name of Newspaper: _____

   • Date: _____

   • Headline: _____

   • Byline: _____

   • Photo Caption: _____

   • Quote by the Captain: _____

3. What is the purpose of the text?

   _____

4. Why did Mrs. Sue say, "It has restored my faith in the cruise line!"?

   _____

5. What impact will the newspaper article have on the cruise line? Why?

   _____

D.   Fill in the information and complete the encyclopedia entry about a cruise ship.

Text Type: _____

Entry: _____

Diagram Title: _____

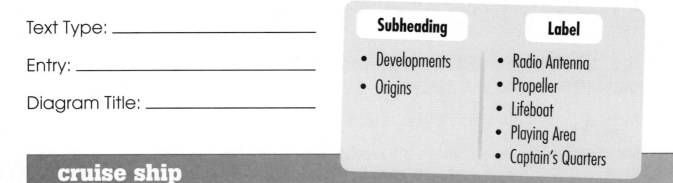

Subheading	Label
• Developments	• Radio Antenna
• Origins	• Propeller
	• Lifeboat
	• Playing Area
	• Captain's Quarters

cruise ship

cruise ship – A cruise ship is a floating vessel used to carry passengers for luxury or pleasure voyages. It provides services and amenities like a hotel.

_____

The first vessel, designed by Albert Ballin specifically for luxury cruising, was built in 1900.

_____

To attract more passengers, ocean liners offering luxury updates to take passengers from one point to another were built. Nowadays, advancements in technology ensure comfortable cruise vacations for passengers. Most cruise lines take passengers on journeys beginning and ending at the same port.

Features of a Cruise Ship

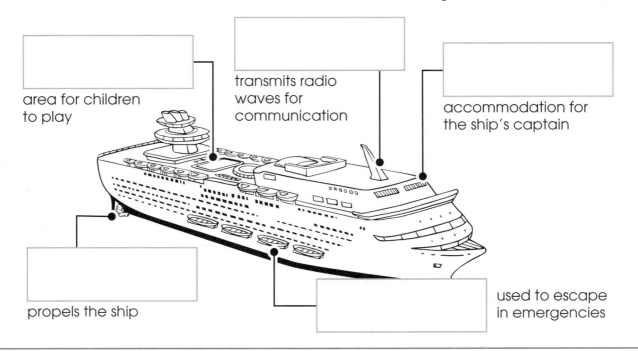

area for children to play

transmits radio waves for communication

accommodation for the ship's captain

propels the ship

used to escape in emergencies

E. Create a leaflet to advertise a cruise vacation using as many features of a leaflet as possible.

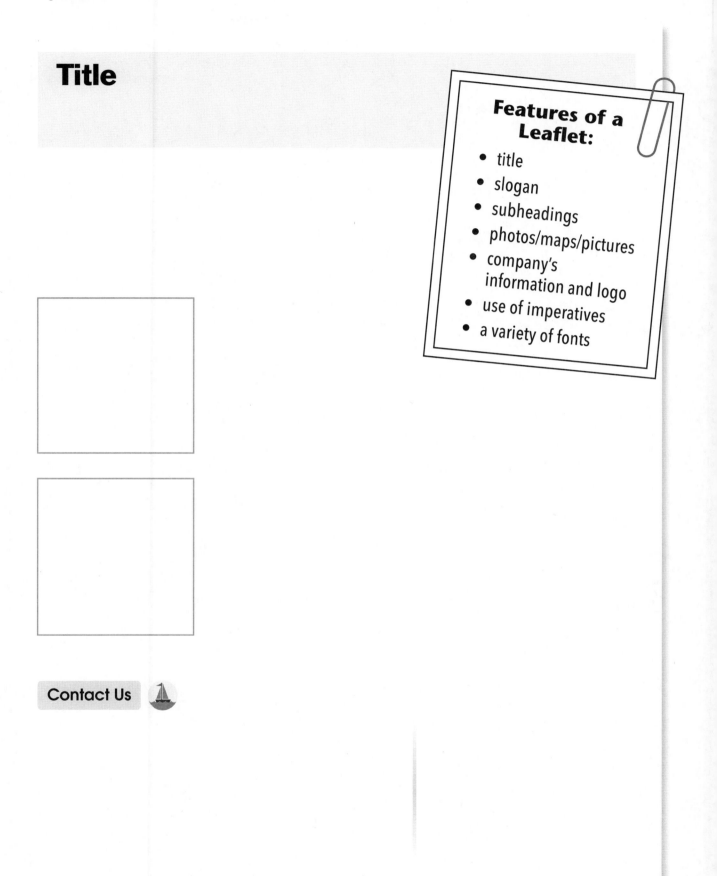

Title

Features of a Leaflet:

- title
- slogan
- subheadings
- photos/maps/pictures
- company's information and logo
- use of imperatives
- a variety of fonts

Contact Us

Complete EnglishSmart (Grade 5)

1.1 Treasures of the Orient

In the 13th century, trade between Europe and Asia was channelled through the "Silk Route", the trade route from China to Constantinople (now Istanbul). The Muslims controlled and restricted trade with the East and the merchants of the Mediterranean were completely cut off from the established trade route. The European merchants wanted the silk, spices, and gold found in the East. So important was this market that the Europeans were willing to go to great expense and trouble to find new trade routes.

The Polo family, merchants from Venice, made the trip to China. It was part of a 14-year excursion. They wanted to bring back marketable goods to be sold in Venice. At the request of the Chinese ruler, the great Kublai Khan, they were to return to China and bring back scholars with them. Kublai Khan was interested in learning about the European culture.

The Polo family set out for China in 1271 for what was to be a four-year journey. They crossed Asia Minor (Turkey) and Persia (present-day Iran and Iraq). They stayed for nearly a year in northern Afghanistan, likely because of illness. Their journey took them across the Himalayan mountains and the Gobi Desert and finally to Shangdu (present-day Beijing), where they were reunited with Kublai Khan.

The Polos stayed in China for another 17 years and became very wealthy. Marco Polo recorded the events of his travels in a book that told of the riches of the Orient. It was his book that inspired the Europeans to share in the wealth by finding a trade route by water that would be quick and profitable. The race to discover a trade route was officially launched.

1.2

1. Who controlled the trade with the East?

   A. the Muslim merchants

   B. the European merchants

2. What were the Polo family?

   A. They were scholars.

   B. They were merchants.

3. What did Kublai Khan want the Polos to bring back from Europe?

   A. marketable goods

   B. scholars

4. What did Marco Polo's book inspire others to do?

   A. to find a trade route by water

   B. to explore China

2.1 Pirates of the Caribbean

Pirates, like Captain Henry Morgan, were also referred to as buccaneers. They became legendary as stories about their ruthlessness and their skills at pirating spread throughout the Caribbean and to the southern coast of North America. The most notorious pirate of them all was Edward Teach, better known as Blackbeard. He was tall and muscular with a long beard braided with bright ribbons that hung down to his chest. He was a fearful sight. When he went into battle, he would put slow burning fuses in his hair, creating a smoky haze that surrounded his head. If his opponents put up a fight, he would teach them a lesson. In one case, he cut off the nose of a Portuguese sailor; in another, he killed one of his own crew members just to remind people of how evil he was. It was acts like these that spread his reputation far and wide and made piracy easy for him.

Piracy was taking its toll on the economy of the major trading countries. Doing business in the Caribbean and the Carolina coast was becoming very expensive. The Governor of Virginia, Alexander Spotswood, put up a reward of £100 (approximately US$160) for the capture of Blackbeard. This amount was roughly ten years' wages for a sailor at the time.

A British naval officer named Maynard took up the challenge with a crew of 60, and found Blackbeard hiding in a North Carolina inlet. The next day, Maynard attacked Blackbeard and on the second attack found himself face to face with the fearsome pirate. Maynard shot him but Blackbeard did not fall. They then fought with swords, and just as Blackbeard was about to deliver a fatal blow, one of Maynard's crew shot and killed him.

With Blackbeard's death came the end of piracy. However, the governor refused to give Maynard the reward of £100. Instead he gave him only £3 (US$5) and half of that to his crew. This paltry payment was hardly worth risking their lives.

2.2

1. What is a buccaneer?

   A. a pirate

   B. a captain

2. What was the real name of Blackbeard?

   A. Henry Morgan

   B. Edward Teach

3. What did the Governor of Virginia do to deal with piracy?

   A. He advised traders not to travel by sea.

   B. He put up a reward for the capture of Blackbeard.

4. Where was Blackbeard killed?

   A. in North Carolina

   B. in Virginia

3.1 Mae Jemison – a Great Inspiration

Mae C. Jemison fulfilled a lifelong dream by becoming the first African-American woman to go into space. This accomplishment did not come easily – it was the result of years of preparation, hard work, and perseverance.

Jemison was born on October 17, 1956 in Decatur, Alabama, and was the youngest of three children. Thanks to one of her uncles, who introduced her to the world of science, Jemison developed interests in anthropology, archaeology, and astronomy at an early age. In 1977, she graduated from Stanford University with degrees in chemical engineering and Afro-American studies. She earned a medical degree from Cornell University in 1981. The following year, Jemison was selected by NASA (National Aeronautics and Space Administration) with 14 others to undergo astronaut training. Then, in 1987, she was accepted into NASA's astronaut program, ready for the space mission. On September 12, 1992, her dream was finally realized. She flew on Space Shuttle Endeavour as the Mission Specialist and spent eight days in space before returning to Earth on September 20, 1992.

Jemison is a compassionate person. She has worked as a volunteer providing medical service in a Cambodian refugee camp and as a medical officer with the Peace Corps in West Africa. She is multi-talented, too. In addition to English, Jemison speaks fluent Russian, Japanese, and Swahili. She has even appeared on an episode of the TV show "Star Trek: The Next Generation". Jemison founded the International Science Camp in Chicago in 1994, a program designed to stimulate children's interest in science and space.

3.2

1. What did Jemison study at Stanford University?

   A. anthropology and astronomy
   B. chemical engineering and Afro-American studies

2. Which program did Jemison join in 1987?

   A. Stanford's astronomy program   B. NASA's astronaut program

3. Which space shuttle did Jemison fly on?

   A. Space Shuttle Discovery   B. Space Shuttle Endeavour

4. What is the listing purpose of the International Science Camp?

   A. to stimulate children's interest in science and space
   B. to test children's knowledge of science and space

4.1 Bicycles – Then and Now

The modern bicycle, such as the models used in the world's most famous bike race – the Tour de France, is light, fast, durable, comfortable, and well-equipped. Original bicycles, however, were very simple mechanical devices.

The first bicycle appeared in the early 19th century. It was Pierre Michaux, a Frenchman from Paris, and his son who built the first bicycle to be mass-marketed. They added pedals to the front wheel of their basic bicycle, thus allowing for propulsion. This design, which was named the "velocipede", resembled the tricycle used by children today. It was a vast improvement over the standard two-wheeler of the time and before long, sales reached 500 units per year – a number considered high by standards of that time.

The next advancement was to make the front wheel larger to improve speed. In 1887, the "safety" bicycle was designed to address safety issues by reducing the size of the front wheel. This model introduced the use of the chain which, when attached by two chainwheels, rotated the back wheel instead of the front. This mechanical principle of volition was based on the ratio between the number of teeth of the front chainwheel to that on the back sprocket. If, for example, the front chainwheel had 32 teeth and the rear sprocket 8, then the ratio would be 32:8; this meant that for every rotation of the front cogwheel, there were four rotations of the rear one – a ratio of 4 to 1. Consequently, the bicycle could have wheels of equal measure and actually increase speed.

One of the most important advancements of the safety bicycle was the addition of gears. This allowed for the use of different gears for particular situations. A "derailleur" would shift the chain from one sprocket to another, creating a new pairing of chainwheels with different ratios of teeth, and therefore, various levels of pedalling difficulty.

As a result of pollution and environmental concerns, there has been renewed interest in biking in cities worldwide.

4.2

1. What is the Tour de France?
   A. a model of the modern bicycle
   B. a famous bike race

2. What did Pierre Michaux and his son build?
   A. the tricycle
   B. the velocipede

3. Why were pedals added to the basic bicycle?
   A. to allow for propulsion
   B. to make the bicycle more durable

4. What were two features of the safety bicycle?
   A. a smaller front wheel and the addition of gears
   B. a larger front wheel and a safety brake

5.1 **Meat-eating Plants**

Plants are bright, colourful adornments of nature that feed on sunlight and water. Or so we think. Many plants are, in fact, carnivorous. Science fiction movies have frightened us with horror stories of human-eating plants that swallow human beings whole. This notion may seem absurd to us, but it is an ugly truth for many an unsuspecting insect.

Some species of plants require the meat of an insect as a dietary supplement. There are two types of meat-eating plants. Some plants such as the Venus Flytrap actually move to capture their prey. Other plants sit and wait and let the insects trap themselves. The Sticky Sundew is covered with sticky hairs that produce a type of glue that sticks to the unsuspecting insect when it lands. The hairs then close over it and it is absorbed into the plant. The Cobra Lily, named for its snake-like appearance, lures insects with its nectar. Once an insect enters the plant, it becomes confused by the light shining through the leaves. Following this light to escape, it becomes exhausted and drops into the liquid of the plant.

The best known predator plant is the Venus Flytrap. Insects are attracted by the unusual leaf tips and cannot resist landing on them. Adding to this lure is the promise of food from sweet smelling nectar. After the insect lands on the surface of the leaf, two kidney-shaped lobes, triggered by the sensitive bristles at the top of the leaf, snap shut. After about half an hour, the Venus Flytrap will secrete enzymes and acids which will slowly digest the insect. Full digestion of an insect may take up to two weeks and the trap will then be prepared for another victim. When the Venus Flytrap is ready to eat again, the trap opens and the exoskeleton of the devoured insect is blown away in the wind.

5.2

1. Why are some plants considered carnivorous?
   - A. They eat insects as a dietary supplement.
   - B. They swallow human beings whole.

2. Which two plants use nectar to attract insects?
   - A. the Venus Flytrap and the Cobra Lily
   - B. the Cobra Lily and the Sticky Sundew

3. Why are insects attracted to the Venus Flytrap?
   - A. They have unusual leaf tips.
   - B. They are pretty and colourful.

4. How long does it take the Venus Flytrap to digest a whole insect?
   - A. about half an hour
   - B. about two weeks

R1.1 The "Horseless Carriage"

After the first modern automobile was built by the German engineer Karl Benz, the next step was to figure out a way to mass-produce it. The goal was to build automobiles in such a way that it was cost-effective so that the money saved in manufacturing could be passed on to the consumers. As a result, there would be a reasonably priced car that everyone could own.

In 1893, an American named Henry Ford built his first car based on the Benz model. Benz continued to build expensive cars in Europe for upper class purchasers. Ford had a better idea. He wanted to build cars for everyone. Ford visited a slaughterhouse and watched as the butchers cut the cattle up in an assembly line with each station chopping off a particular portion of the beef. Ford decided to apply this method to the production of cars and the automobile assembly line was born – a method still used today.

In 1908, Ford produced the Model T, which was a simple family car without the fancy trappings found on expensive cars. In 1913, he created his assembly line and the cars began to roll out. The more he produced, the lower the prices were until he managed to get the price of his Model T down to about $285. In 1914, Ford paid his workers an incredible $5 per day. That was nearly twice the average wage for similar work at that time. Professionals declared that this was a ridiculously high wage and that he would go bankrupt. Ford reasoned that if he paid his workers enough money, they could afford to buy his cars. By 1924, Ford had sold two million cars.

Ford created mass production but it was General Motors that understood marketing. They introduced the yearly model change which enticed buyers to purchase the latest style of car. They also introduced the "payment plan" whereby a buyer could purchase a car on credit and make monthly payments. People love the automobile because of the sense of freedom and excitement it gives.

R1.2

1. Who wanted to build cars that everyone could afford to buy?
   A. Henry Ford   B. Karl Benz

2. Where did Henry Ford get the idea for the automobile assembly line?
   A. a slaughterhouse   B. a factory

3. What kind of car was the Model T?
   A. an expensive car with fancy trappings   B. a simple family car

4. Why did Ford pay his workers high wages?
   A. He wanted them to be able to buy his cars.
   B. He was grateful for their hard work.

Answers

1   Treasures of the Orient

A. 1. A   2. D   3. C   4. B
B. 1. A   2. B   3. B   4. A
C. 1. Silk Route   2. silk ; gold
   3. Kublai Khan   4. Persia
   5. Shangdu
D. 1. A new trade route was needed because the European merchants wanted the silk, spices, and gold found in the East. However, the only trade route between Europe and Asia, the "Silk Route", was controlled by the Muslim merchants.
   2. The Polos travelled through Asia Minor (Turkey), Persia (present-day Iran and Iraq), northern Afghanistan, the Himalayan mountains, and the Gobi Desert, finally arriving in Shangdu (present-day Beijing).
   3. (Suggested answer)
      The Polo family learned about the riches of the Orient as they became very wealthy in China. Marco Polo wrote a book about the riches of the Orient, which inspired the Europeans to share in this wealth by finding a new trade route by water.
E. (Individual summary)

2   Pirates of the Caribbean

A. 1. B   2. D   3. C   4. C
B. 1. A   2. B   3. B   4. A
C. 1. T   2. F   3. F   4. T
   5. F   6. T   7. F   8. F
D. 1. Blackbeard was tall and muscular with a long beard braided with bright ribbons that hung down to his chest. He was a fearful sight.
   2. The reward was not worth it because it was a paltry payment compared to what was promised. Maynard and his crew could have made just as much money as sailors and captains without risking their lives to capture Blackbeard.
E. (Individual summary)

3   Mae Jemison – a Great Inspiration

A. 1. B   2. A   3. A   4. B
B. 1. B   2. B   3. B   4. A
C. Stanford
   1981 ; medical
   NASA
   1987 ; astronaut
   1992
   Chicago
D. 1. On September 12, 1992, Mae Jemison flew on Space Shuttle Endeavour as the Mission Specialist and spent eight days in space before returning to Earth on September 20, 1992.
   2. Jemison is a compassionate person because she has worked as a volunteer providing medical service in a Cambodian refugee camp and as a medical officer with the Peace Corps in West Africa.
E. (Individual summary)

4   Bicycles – Then and Now

A. 1. D   2. B   3. A   4. A
B. 1. B   2. B   3. A   4. A
C. 1. 19th century – the first bicycle appeared
   2. 1887 – the safety bicycle was designed
   3. 32 teeth – the front chainwheel
   4. 8 teeth – the rear sprocket
   5. 4 to 1 – the ratio of gears
   6. derailleur – shifts the chain
D. 1. Original bicycles were simple mechanical devices compared to the modern bicycle, which is light, fast, durable, comfortable, and well-equipped.
   2. Gears were added to the safety bicycle to allow for the use of different gears for particular situations, which allowed for various levels of pedaling difficulty and enhanced safety.

3. (Suggested answer)
   1. Cycling is good for the environment as it does not cause pollution.
   2. Cycling can be used for exercise and therefore helps improve health.
   3. Cycling is a fun activity.

E. (Individual summary)

5   Meat-eating Plants

A. 1. A   2. B   3. C   4. D
B. 1. A   2. A   3. A   4. B
C. 1. carnivorous
   2. insects
   3. dietary
   4. Venus Flytrap
   5. prey
   6. Sticky Sundew
D. 1. Science fiction movies have frightened us with horror stories of human-eating plants that swallow human beings whole.
   2. There are two types of meat-eating plants. The first type, such as the Venus Flytrap, moves to catch its prey, while the second type, such as the Sticky Sundew, sits and waits for the insects to trap themselves.
   3. When an insect, attracted by the unusual leaf tips of the Venus Flytrap, lands on the surface of its leaf, two kidney-shaped lobes, triggered by the sensitive bristles at the top of the leaf, snap shut. After about half an hour, the Venus Flytrap secretes enzymes and acids that slowly digest the insect.
E. (Individual summary)

Review 1

A. 1. Karl Benz
   2. cost-effective
   3. 1893
   4. 1908

5. lower the prices became
6. $285
7. $5 per day
8. 2 million
9. marketing
10. freedom and excitement

B. 1. A   2. A   3. B   4. A
C. family ; Benz ; automobile ; cost-effective ; assembly line ; slaughterhouse ; manufacturing
D. 1. 1913 – the year in which Ford created his assembly line
   2. 1908 – the year in which Ford's family car was introduced
   3. everyone – Ford's target consumers
   4. expensive cars – built by Benz
   5. yearly model change – introduced by General Motors
   6. upper class purchasers in Europe – Benz's target consumers
E. 1. T   2. F   3. T   4. F
   5. T   6. F   7. T
F. 1.   2.   3. ✔   4. ✔
   5.   6. ✔
G. 1. The first modern automobile was built by Karl Benz.
   2. In 1908, Ford created the Model T, a family car without the fancy trappings found on expensive cars.
   3. The more cars Henry Ford produced, the lower the prices became.
   4. By 1924, Ford had sold two million cars.
   5. Ford managed to get the price of the Model T down to $285.
H. 1. General Motors introduced the yearly model change to entice buyers to purchase the latest style of car. They also introduced the "payment plan" so a buyer could purchase a car on credit and make monthly payments.
   2. Some professionals thought Ford would go bankrupt because he paid his workers nearly twice the average wage for similar work at that time.
I. (Individual summary)

1 Nouns

A. Countable Noun:
sister ; aunt ; cousin ; airport ; week ; week ;
vacation ; relatives ; time ; city

Uncountable Noun:
scenery ; excitement

Proper Noun:
Dublin ; Cork City ; Ring of Kerry ; Ireland ; London ;
Buckingham Palace

B. 1. bunch
   2. deck
   3. herd
   4. swarm
   5. team

C. 1. singular
   2. singular
   3. plural
   4. plural
   5. singular
   6. singular
   7. plural
   8. singular

D. Melinda had been suffering from a minor <u>illness</u>.
   As her <u>health</u> improved, her mother saw it as
   an <u>opportunity</u> to fulfill her <u>dream</u> of visiting a
   haunted castle.
   Full of <u>excitement</u> and <u>fear</u>, they arrived at
   the castle. Melinda held onto her favourite
   necklace for <u>luck</u> as she stepped inside. She
   was able to rely on her <u>bravery</u> and <u>confidence</u>
   as she made her way through a web of scary
   spiders and spooky ghosts! Finally, she realized
   that she could overcome anything if she
   remained calm and determined.
   Feeling: excitement ; fear
   Idea: opportunity ; dream ; luck
   Quality: bravery ; confidence
   State: illness ; health

E. (Individual writing)

2 Direct and Indirect Objects

A. 1. The pianist <u>played</u> a wonderful (song) at the
      beginning of the event.
   2. Lucy <u>ate</u> the entire (cake) in the kitchen after
      school.
   3. Carly <u>wore</u> a pretty (dress) to the party last
      night.
   4. Andy <u>ordered</u> some (gifts) from an online
      company.
   5. Emma's dog <u>catches</u> the (Frisbee) with his big
      mouth.
   6. The farmer <u>ploughed</u> his (fields) in the morning.
   7. The guest speaker <u>is giving</u> a (speech) on the
      ancient Egyptian civilization.
   8. Samuel <u>bought</u> some (drinks) for the birthday
      party.
   9. The teacher <u>opened</u> the (windows) to let in
      some fresh air.
   10. Dad <u>parked</u> his (car) in the driveway last night.
   11. The choir <u>sang</u> melodious (songs) in the
       concert.

B. 1. ✔   2. ✗
   3. ✗   4. ✔
   5. ✔   6. ✗
   7. ✗   8. ✗
   9. ✔   10. ✗
   11. ✗   12. ✔

C. 1. direct
   2. direct
   3. indirect
   4. indirect
   5. direct
   6. direct
   7. indirect
   8. indirect

D. bicycle ; top ; himself ; drink

  Colour green: bicycle ; top ; drink

  Colour red: himself

E. It was a dark and stormy night. Emily had just finished reading her <u>book</u> (D) and wanted to get <u>herself</u> (I) a <u>snack</u> (D) from the kitchen. Other than her cat and the occasional field mouse, the house was empty. Only the sound of leaves rustling outside could be heard. When Emily reached the <u>bottom of the staircase</u> (D), she saw a <u>mouse</u> (D) scurrying around the corner. Normally, this would not have given <u>her</u> (I) the <u>creeps</u> (D), but on this particular night, Emily had an eerie <u>feeling</u> (D) that the mouse was trying to tell <u>her</u> (I) <u>something</u> (D). It stared at her and she did not know how to react. Then suddenly, she felt a <u>wisp of air</u> (D) over her head. Emily turned around to see what had brought <u>home</u> (I) the <u>wind</u> (D). It was her cat. It had leapt from the staircase railing, wearing the <u>cape</u> (D) that Emily had put on it earlier. The mouse gave <u>the cat</u> (I) a startled <u>look</u> (D) and scurried away.

3   Pronouns

A. 1. he (in blue)

  2. I (in blue)

  3. him (in red)

  4. She (in blue)

  5. We (in blue) ; she (in blue) ; us (in red)

  6. They (in blue) ; me (in red)

  7. she (in blue) ; it (in red)

  8. I (in blue) ; him (in red)

  9. He (in blue) ; it (in red)

B. 1. It ; S

  2. him ; O

  3. her ; O

  4. He ; S ; They ; S

  5. me ; O

  6. She ; S

  7. It ; S

  8. I ; S ; them ; O

C. 1. Danny made <u>himself</u> a big, yummy breakfast.   ✔

  2. Maggie taught ~~itself~~ how to skate. *herself*   ○

  3. I wash ~~ourselves~~ when I get up in the morning. *myself*   ○

  4. "Did you make this card ~~himself~~?" Mrs. Robin asked her son. *yourself*   ○

  5. The little mice hid ~~itself~~ behind the piano when they saw the cat. *themselves*   ○

  6. Emma set <u>herself</u> an impossible task at the beginning of the year.   ✔

  7. After we fell, we picked ~~yourself~~ up with Ms. Hall's encouragement. *ourselves*   ○

  8. The bird built <u>itself</u> a nest in the tree early this morning.   ✔

  9. "Don't get ~~myself~~ into trouble again!" Mr. Morris reminded us. *yourselves*   ○

  10. My sister and I had to look after ~~herself~~ last night because Mom and Dad were not home. *ourselves*   ○

  11. Gina and Dennis treated <u>themselves</u> to ice cream sundaes after a long day of hard work.   ✔

D. 1. She told him her name.

  2. He ate them in the kitchen.

  3. They found it yesterday.

  4. We will meet her at the entrance.

E. (Individual writing)

4   Modal Verbs

A. A: can   B: can't   C: can

  D: can   E: cannot   F: can

  G: cannot   H: can ; cannot   I: Can

  Ability: A ; B ; D ; F ; H

  Permission: C ; E ; G ; I

B. 1. could ; PO
   2. could ; A
   3. could ; P
   4. could ; P
   5. could ; A
   6. could ; A
   7. could ; P
   8. could ; PO

C. (Suggested answers)
   1. Will
   2. Would
   3. Could
   4. Will

D. (Suggested answers)
   A: Could you please pass the salt?
   B: Would you please get me a glass of water?
   C: Will you please get my kite out of the tree?

5   Simple and Progressive Tenses

A. 1. Look! The children <u>run</u> toward the ice cream truck.
        are running

2. Bernie <u>is singing</u> a pretty song every morning.
        sings

3. Nicky <u>shows</u> Jack her new running shoes now.
        is showing

4. Listen! The breeze <u>blows</u> through the trees in the forest.
        is blowing

5. Shelby <u>is looking</u> after her baby sister whenever her mother is out.
        looks

6. "I can't talk to you now. I <u>drive</u>," Dad said.
        am driving

7. Mrs. Watt <u>is reading</u> her son a bedtime story every night.
        reads

8. Bobby <u>is giving</u> his dog a bath once every three weeks.
        gives

B. 1. was flying
   2. talked
   3. was walking
   4. was rehearsing
   5. played
   6. was taking
   7. was eating
   8. spotted ; decided

C. 1. Many of us will watch the parade on TV.
   2. The phone will ring in five minutes.
   3. Vinnie's cousin will be visiting for the summer.
   4. There will be a new radio program on Monday morning.
   5. Marty will be attending a different school for some time.
   6. Karl's children will play one more game before they have to leave.
   7. Since it is so hot, they will be swimming until sunset.

D. 1. The boy eats an egg every day.
   2. The farmers are milking their cows now.
   3. The teachers had a meeting yesterday.
   4. They were playing soccer all day.
   5. Stephanie and Aiden will buy a cookbook for their mother tomorrow.
   6. Sam will be mowing the lawn the entire afternoon on Saturday.

6   Perfect Tenses

A. 1. ✔
   2. ✔
   3.
   4.
   5.
   6. ✔
   7. ✔
   8. ✔
   9. ✔
   10.
   11. ✔

B. 1. had studied
2. had finished
3. had gone
4. had landed
5. had taken
6. had cleaned
7. had eaten
8. had knocked
9. had played
10. had practised

C. 1. <u>has decided</u> ; recently
2. <u>had waited</u> ; before
3. <u>has worked</u> ; for
4. <u>had not</u> ; <u>finished</u> ; yet
5. <u>had</u> ; <u>started</u> ; just
6. <u>have</u> ; <u>played</u> ; never
7. <u>has played</u> ; since
8. <u>Have</u> ; <u>been</u> ; ever
9. <u>has</u> ; <u>painted</u> ; so far
10. <u>had started</u> ; after
11. <u>had</u> ; <u>begun</u> ; already

D. (Individual writing)

7   Active and Passive Voice

A.

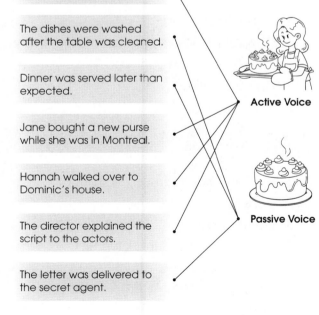

Jason played with his dog in the backyard.

The dishes were washed after the table was cleared.

Dinner was served later than expected.

Jane bought a new purse while she was in Montreal.

Hannah walked over to Dominic's house.

The director explained the script to the actors.

The letter was delivered to the secret agent.

Active Voice

Passive Voice

B. Active Voice: 2, 5, 7, 9, 10, 11
Passive Voice: 1, 3, 4, 6, 8, 12

C. 1. was put
2. were told
3. was given
4. was drawn
5. be seen
6. were provided
7. were offered
8. was served
9. were lent
10. were handed

D. 1. The flowers were watered yesterday.
2. The invaluable antiques were stolen.
3. The whole story was repeated to the detectives.
4. Natalie's scarf was blown away.
5. Many toys were donated to the charity group.
6. The book was written in 2015.

8   Direct and Indirect Speech

A. 1. "Wait! I don't want to be late for school!" Liz cried as she ran after the bus.
2. "Everybody deserves a second chance!" the kind lady said.
3. "Call me again tomorow," said Mom.
4. The elves cheered, "Long live King Julian!"
5. "Jason, do you want butter or jam?" asked Mrs. Brown.
6. The teacher instructed, "Write your name on the first page of the book."
7. Trisha said, "Fish soup is my favourite on a cold winter day."
8. "The coffee is not hot enough!" the customer complained.
9. "You can find the information on the website," Karen answered.
10. "I heard some noises from the kitchen," Daniel whispered.
11. "Let's go jogging in the park tomorrow morning," Dad suggested.
12. Little Kate asked curiously, "Can your puppy swim?"

B. 1. "Is your friend going with you?" (asked) Mom.
    2. "Cats have nine lives," Quincy (whispered) to Nora.
    3. "The thieves took everything!" (mourned) the woman.
    4. Sharon (told) her dad, "I made a new friend today!"
    5. "Watch out! Don't step on my truck!" Alan's brother (screamed).
    6. Larry (confessed), "I've broken your favourite mug, Mom."
    7. "I don't like pineapple on pizza," Jay (complained) to his friend.
    8. The suspect (replied), "I wasn't in town when the burglary took place."
    9. "Let's go to the cottage this weekend," Pansy (suggested).
    10. Peter (says), "Your ice cream cone looks really good."

C. 1. ?   2. ,   3. !   4. ?
    5. .   6. !   7. .   8. .
    9. ?   10. !   11. ?   12. ,

D. 1. liked
    2. Jeromy complained ; was
    3. she did not know the answer
    4. The children said that they needed a break.

9   Adjectives

A. 1. safer ; safest
    2. tinier
    3. saddest
    4. greater ; greatest
    5. friendlier ; friendliest
    6. most forgetful
    7. more influential
    8. bigger ; biggest
    9. happier ; happiest
    10. nicer ; nicest
    11. livelier ; liveliest
    12. thinner ; thinnest

B. 1. Marie's room is the tidiest in the house.
    2. We had the most splendid dinner in Little Italy.
    3. Kim's mother makes the smoothest cheesecake I have ever had.
    4. This restaurant is more popular than the one beside it.
    5. Marcus is usually faster than Gilbert.
    6. Canada is the most beautiful country in the world!
    7. Judy is the tallest girl in her class.
    8. Bella was more careful than her cousin Robin.
    9. This light is a bit dimmer than the others.
    10. I think soccer is more exciting than hockey!

C. 1. scared
    2. moving
    3. charming
    4. relaxing
    5. surprised ; locked
    6. encouraging
    7. ripped
    8. worried
    9. deafening
    10. alarming
    11. excited

D. A: confusing ; confused
    B: boring ; bored
    C: interesting ; interested
    D: tiring ; tired
    (Suggested answer)
    A: Charlotte's reasoning was confusing. Everyone in the group was confused.
    (Individual writing)

10   Adverbs

A. 1. more cautiously ; most cautiously
    2. earlier ; earliest
    3. worse ; worst
    4. farther/further ; farthest/furthest
    5. quicker ; quickest
    6. more often ; most often
    7. better ; best

B. 1. fastest   2. higher
   3. most convincingly   4. earlier
   5. slower
C. 1. more frequently
   2. later
   3. sooner
   4. earliest
   5. most often
   6. most confidently
   7. faster ; more neatly
   8. closer
   9. farther
   10. most clearly
D. 1. ✔
          more lightly
   2. The fairy walked <u>most lightly</u> than the elf.
          more calmly
   3. She dealt with emergencies <u>calmer</u> than Yan.
          farther
   4. The dog ran <u>farthest</u> into the forest than the cat.
   5. ✔
          softest
   6. Of all the children, Jayce spoke <u>softer</u>.
          harder
   7. After failing the test, Sophie worked <u>hardest</u> than before.
          highest
   8. That frog jumps <u>most highly</u> even though it is the smallest one over there.
          worst
   9. I sing <u>worse</u> in my family but I like singing.
   10. ✔
          more gracefully
   11. Alana danced <u>most gracefully</u> than the other ballerinas.
   12. ✔
E. 1. more brightly ; most brightly ; more brightly ; most brightly
   2. nearer ; nearest (Individual writing)
   3. more carefully ; most carefully (Individual writing)
   4. later ; latest (Individual writing)

11   **Phrases**

A. 1. subject
   2. complement
   3. object
   4. complement
   5. complement
   6. object
   7. subject
B. 1. Adjective Phrase
   2. Adverb Phrase
   3. Adverb Phrase
   4. Adjective Phrase
   5. Adverb Phrase
   6. Adjective Phrase
   7. Adverb Phrase
   8. Adjective Phrase
C. 1. to go to the amusement park
   2. to ride on the roller-coaster
   3. to ride on the carousel
   4. to sit down on
   5. to get some food
   6. to share some fries with Kim and Rachel
D. 1. P
   2. O
   3. S
   4. C
   5. S

12   **Clauses**

A. 1. (Colour in green.)
   2. (Colour in green.)
   3. (Colour in green.)
   4. (Colour in yellow.)
   5. (Colour in yellow.)
   6. (Colour in yellow.)
   7. (Colour in yellow.)
   8. (Colour in green.)
   9. (Colour in yellow.)

B.

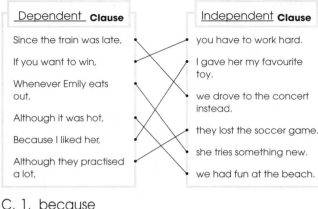

Dependent **Clause**	Independent **Clause**
Since the train was late,	you have to work hard.
If you want to win,	I gave her my favourite toy.
Whenever Emily eats out,	we drove to the concert instead.
Although it was hot,	they lost the soccer game.
Because I liked her,	she tries something new.
Although they practised a lot,	we had fun at the beach.

C. 1. because
2. while
3. if
4. and

D. 1. Adv.   2. Adj.
3. Adv.   4. Adv.
5. Adj.   6. Adj.
7. Adj.   8. Adv.

E. (Individual writing)

13 Sentences

A. 1. My family loves skiing in winter.
2. The sun rises every morning.
3. Sophia's cat was very lazy.
4. We drove through Georgia.
5. Catherine quickly walked toward the teddy bear.
6. Everyone went to Karen's party yesterday.
7. Audrey was very excited about the circus.
8. Mrs. Stow did not want to cook today.

B. 1. <u>He is as strong as an ox</u> but <u>he would not hurt a flea</u>.
2. <u>I can go shopping tomorrow</u> but <u>I have to be home by 5 p.m.</u>
3. <u>I need to catch the next bus</u> or <u>I will have to walk to school</u>.
4. <u>Adam and Andrew studied very hard for their test</u> and <u>they are proud of their high marks</u>.
5. <u>The baseball game was cancelled today</u> but <u>the teams will play tomorrow</u>.
6. <u>We will catch a movie tonight</u> or <u>we will visit our friends</u>.

C. A: but ; I want to ride my bike but it is raining outside.
B: and ; I saw a shooting star and I wished for a new piano!

D. 1. ✗ ; before it was time for bed
2. ✔
3. ✔
4. ✗ ; while they were waiting for their turn
5. ✔
6. ✗ ; If you do not give up
7. ✗ ; until Dad played with her
8. ✔
9. ✔
10. ✗ ; unless you have other suggestions
11. ✔

E. 1. Simple   2. Simple
3. Complex   4. Compound
5. Simple   6. Simple
7. Complex   8. Complex
9. Compound   10. Compound

14 Punctuation

A. Correct Sentence: 1 ; 4 ; 6
Incorrect Sentence: 2 ; 3 ; 5
Rewritten Sentence:
2 ; Kevin, can you please help me?
3 ; Pepper, my dog, knows a lot of tricks.
5 ; "I am going for a walk," said Taylor.

B. 1. Ivy has three items on her birthday list**:** a telescope, drawing pencils, and a new dress.
2. There was one problem with Robert's plan**:** he did not have enough money to buy the material.
3. Never take school for granted**:** some children never get the chance to attend.
4. There are four foods Stephen does not like to eat**:** beans, pork, salmon, and bananas.
5. Little Ava solved the puzzles within minutes**:** intelligence is not determined by age.
6. I have read several genres of books**:** drama, mystery, and science fiction.

C. (Individual writing)

D. 1. Daisy said she will be late for dinner; she has an appointment.

2. The Mona Lisa is in Paris; I will never see it in person.

3. We cannot wait much longer; we will miss our bus.

4. It is not necessary to bring a gift; it is your presence that is most desired.

5. The last city we visited was Prague; it was my favourite.

6. Jeremy's backyard is large; it is great for running around in.

7. It will rain tomorrow; it will be good for the garden.

E. (Suggested answers)

Ms. Duncan's grade six class went to Kearney for a week-long trip in June. The kids learned a number of things: how to canoe, how to make dream catchers, and how to work in teams. One morning, they stopped by a marsh to learn about insects that live in water. "Let's study these insects," Ms. Duncan said. The camp leaders were glad that every kid had brought insect repellent in tubes; aerosol cans are not good for the environment. Each evening, a leader named Mike would teach the kids a new song – one of which was called, "The Merry Moose" – so the kids could sing on their way back to their cabins afterwards. They also learned about everything they needed to build a campfire: matches or a lighter, tinder, and kindling.

Review 2

A. 1. quality
2. Mary wrote <u>Dan</u> a letter.
3. She always helped <u>them</u>.
4. reflexive pronoun
5. Can
6. I was cooking when he called.
7. future progressive tense
8. present perfect tense
9. yesterday
10. The vase was broken.
11. Claire said that she loved roses.
12. most gigantic
13. loving
14. more often
15. the complement
16. Liam eats <u>very loudly</u>.
17. because
18. Daniel laughed <u>when Chris fell</u>.
19. complex sentence
20. :

B. countable noun: tent
proper noun: Ontario
abstract noun: time
uncountable noun: water
collective noun: family
subject pronoun: He ; we
object pronoun: him ; her
reflexive pronoun: themselves
(Suggested direct and indirect objects)
Mrs. Garcia hands <u>him</u> ⟨pillows, a cooler, and the water⟩.
"You won't need these either," he says to Marissa as he passes <u>her</u> ⟨the movies she wants to bring⟩.

C. The Garcias arrive at the campground and find their campsite by a lake. However, it looks like it <u>could</u> [PO] rain any minute, so Mr. Garcia, who <u>cannot</u> [A] set up the tent alone, says, "Marissa, <u>could</u> [RA] you please lend me a hand?"

After setting up their tent, Mr. Garcia tells Ivan that he <u>could</u> [PE] go fishing with him at sunrise the next day. Ivan's jaw drops open in disappointment.

"<u>Would</u> [RA] you two gather some firewood for dinner?" asks Mrs. Garcia.

"<u>Can</u> [PE] we go home instead?" cries Marissa. She is already wishing she <u>could</u> [PE] watch a movie and she knows Ivan wants to play his video games.

"Seems like the clouds have parted," says Mrs. Garcia. "You two <u>can</u> [PE] go and play nearby after collecting firewood."

"You <u>cannot</u> [PE] miss dinner!" Mrs. Garcia shouts after them as they wearily make their way to the beach to look for firewood.

D. 1. Tense: simple past
   A glistening object was seen on the beach by Ivan and Marissa.
   2. Tense: past continuous
   The object was being carefully examined by Ivan.
   3. Tense: simple future
   The object will be picked up gingerly by them.

E. 1. Ivan (told) his parents
   Ivan told his parents that they had found something interesting on the beach.
   2. Mr. Garcia (exclaimed)
   Mr. Garcia exclaimed that it was an antique brass bottle.
   3. Mrs. Garcia (said)
   Mrs. Garcia said that the bottle looked pretty.
   4. Marissa (guessed)
   Marissa guessed that it might have belonged to a pirate.

F. Noun ; Adjective ;
   Infinitive ; Gerund
   1. Mr. and Mrs. Garcia
   2. very strange
   3. Finding out what is inside
   4. to pry it out
   5. delicately folded ; piece of paper

G.

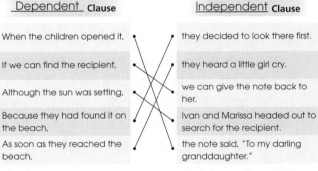

Dependent Clause	Independent Clause
When the children opened it,	they decided to look there first.
If we can find the recipient,	they heard a little girl cry.
Although the sun was setting,	we can give the note back to her.
Because they had found it on the beach,	Ivan and Marissa headed out to search for the recipient.
As soon as they reached the beach,	the note said, "To my darling granddaughter."

H. "Look! That little girl is crying," said Marissa. "I'm going to help her." Approaching gently, Marissa asked the girl, "Why are you so sad?"
"I've lost my grandma's brass bottle; it was beautiful and unique," replied the girl.
"Don't be upset – we found a brass bottle that contained a note. Here, see if it's yours," offered Ivan, giving her the bottle.
Clara, the little girl, thanked them because it was her lost bottle!
All the children played together and Ivan and Marissa could not help loving their camping vacation!
Simple: 1
Compound: 3
Complex: 2

1 Nature Words

A. 1. E
  2. D
  3. F
  4. I
  5. B
  6. G
  7. H
  8. A
  9. C

B. lichens ; shrubs ; soil ; berries ; tundra ; mosses ; scenery ; nature ; Vegetation
  Nunavut's Vegetation – lichens ; shrubs ; berries ; mosses

C. 1. Icebergs can detach from glaciers and float in the open water.
  2. Because the terrain was too rocky, we decided not to go for a hike.
  3. The town is isolated on a plateau projecting upward from the sea.
  4. A brook runs through the woods behind our school.
  5. Compost can be used as nutrition for plants.
  6. A boulder fell from the mountain when the earthquake hit.
  7. We are excited to have a picnic near a forest.
  8. Ice makes cars slip on roads and causes accidents.
  9. We made sandcastles along the coast.

D. (Individual writing)

2 Fire Words

A. 1. ✗ ; blaze
  2. ✔
  3. ✗ ; crackling
  4. ✗ ; roaring
  5. ✗ ; flame
  6. ✔
  7. ✔
  8. ✗ ; fuel

B. 1. twigs ; ignite
  2. extinguish
  3. wood
  4. fuel
  5. flammable
  6. shavings
  7. campfire
  8. blaze

C. sawdust ; wood ; oil ; coal ; bark shavings ; branches ; cloth ; paper ; logs ; gasoline ; propane

D. Fire Type – campfire ; blaze ; inferno ; wildfire ; bonfire
  Fire Sound – crackle ; roar ; snap ; sputter ; pop ; whoosh ; sizzle

E. 1. Torches   2. spark
  3. Heat   4. fireplace
  5. flickered   6. kindle
  7. fireworks

3 Sport Words

A. 1. league – association of teams that play a sport and compete against one another
  2. tournament – sports competition
  3. defenseman – player in a defensive position
  4. rookie – first-year professional sports player
  5. MVP – Most Valuable Player
  6. play-off – extra game played to determine the winner
  7. scout – talent evaluator for professional sports

B. 1. record
  2. forward
  3. goal
  4. player ; rushes
  5. puck
  6. scouts

C. F ; D ; C ; B ; E ; A

D. 1. skiing
  2. basketball
  3. swimming
  4. boxing

E. (Individual writing and drawing)

4 Personality Trait Words

A. agreeable – pleasing
compassionate – thoughtful
considerate – caring
decisive – determined
friendly – amiable
honest – truthful
loyal – faithful
patient – tolerant
sincere – genuine
generous – charitable

B. generous – miserly
pessimistic – optimistic
rash – cautious
hostile – amicable
courteous – rude
cowardly – courageous
cheerful – gloomy
knowledgeable – ignorant
diligent – lazy
decisive – indecisive
deceitful – sincere
Positive: generous ; courteous ; cheerful ;
knowledgeable ; diligent ; decisive ; optimistic ;
courageous ; sincere ; amicable ; cautious
Negative: pessimistic ; rash ; hostile ; cowardly ;
deceitful ; gloomy ; rude ; ignorant ; miserly ;
indecisive ; lazy

C. 1. courageous
2. optimistic
3. rude
4. thoughtful
5. generous
6. determined ; diligent

5 Disaster Words

A. Water Disaster: tsunami, flood
Snow Disaster: avalanche, blizzard
Wind Disaster: windstorm, cyclone, hurricane,
tornado

B. 1. avalanche
2. tornado
3. tsunami
(Individual writing)

C. 1. wildfire
2. drought
3. volcanic eruption
4. (Individual writing and drawing)

D. 1. flood   2. wildfire
3. drought   4. earthquake
5. tsunami   6. avalanche

6 Astronomy Words

A. 1. Aurora Borealis – the Northern Lights
2. constellation – a pattern of stars
3. astronomy – the study of stars and the universe
4. meteor shower – countless shooting stars
5. Milky Way – the name of our galaxy

B. 1. solar system
2. planets ; asteroids
3. constellations
4. galaxy
5. shooting stars
6. meteor shower
7. Northern Lights

C. solar ; eight ; orbit ; planets ; Mercury ; Venus ;
Earth ; Mars ; Jupiter ; Saturn ; Uranus ; Neptune ;
asteroid

D. 1. astronaut – a person who has undergone training in order to travel in a spacecraft

2. comet – an icy celestial object that orbits the sun and can be seen with a bright tail in the night sky

3. rocket – a self-propelling device that can be launched into space

4. Big Dipper – a group of seven bright stars that resemble a dipper and can be used to locate Polaris (the North Star)

E. Solar System:

planet ; sun ; Earth ; Saturn ; comet ; orbit ; asteroid

Group of Stars:

Big Dipper ; galaxy ; constellation ; Milky Way

Human-made Astronomy Device:

rocket ; telescope ; spacecraft

7   Feeling Words

A. 1. ashamed   2. jealous
   3. kind   4. distressed
   5. motivated   6. relieved
   7. shocked   8. confused
   9. proud

B. Positive Feeling:

hopeful, confident, delighted, peaceful, grateful

Negative Feeling:

agonized, irritated, embarrassed, hurt, upset

C. 1. contented
   2. subordinate
   3. exasperated

D. (Individual writing)

8   Feline Words

A. jaguars ; pounced ;
   purr ; stalk ; cheetah ;
   feline; furry ; claws

   1. feline   2. jaguars
   3. purr   4. cheetah
   5. claws   6. stalk
   7. pounced   8. furry

B.

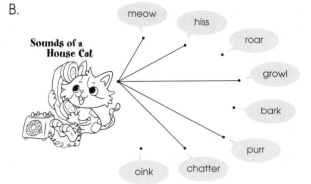

C. There are many different members of the (cat) family. The (snow leopard) is able to camouflage in the white snow in the mountains of central Asia. Another popular member is a short-haired breed of domestic (cat) from Thailand, the (Siamese cat). It is a long-bodied (cat) with slender legs and a long tail.

You would be interested to know that there are animals called "(ligers)". They have a (lion) and a (tiger) as their parents. Therefore, they carry the characteristics of both. (Ligers) also belong to the (cat) family. However, (ligers) are not found in the wild as much as (pumas). The (puma) lives in a variety of habitats all over the world.

D. (Individual drawing and writing)

9   Animal Words

A.

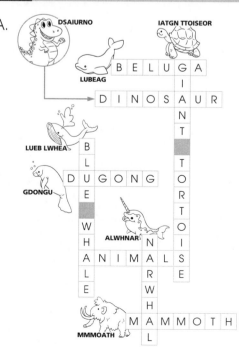

B. Extinct ; Endangered ; Vulnerable ; Near Threatened

(Individual examples)

C. 1. orangutan

2. Malayan tiger

3. sea lion

4. giant panda

D. (Individual drawing and writing)

10 Medical Words

A. 1. a sign of disease

2. a lung infection

3. a type of vaccine

4. medical care given for an illness

5. a disease caused by germs or bacteria

6. an abnormally high body temperature

7. an outbreak of an infectious disease

8. coldness accompanied by shivering

9. a substance injected to prevent a disease

B.

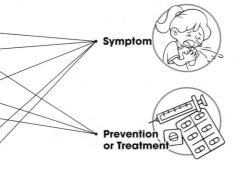

Influenza

fever
chills
vaccine
headaches
flu shot
antibiotics
body aches
loss of appetite

Symptom

Prevention or Treatment

C. 1. cough

2. sore throat

3. fatigue

4. runny nose

5. sneezing

D. 1. influenza   2. Symptoms

3. chills   4. cough

5. Sneezing   6. throat

7. nose   8. pneumonia

9. epidemic   10. treatment

11. antibiotics   12. viruses

13. vaccines   14. shots

11 Archaeology Words

A. 1. C   2. G

3. A   4. H

5. F   6. D

7. B   8. E

9. J   10. I

B. 1. survey   2. excavate

3. classify   4. analyze

5. write   6. present

C. 1. mattock

2. screen

3. trowel

4. file

5. shovel

6. tape measure

7. clippers

8. brush

D. 1. cavemen

2. Fossils ; prehistoric

3. earth ; remains

4. museum

5. relics

6. conservation ; repairing

12 Communication Words

A. Verbal Communication:

consonant, speech, syllable, vowel

Both: language, story

Written Communication:

hieroglyph, logogram, print, symbol

B. 1. phrase – a small group of words as a unit

2. consonant – a basic speech sound that is not a vowel

3. symbol – a mark used to represent an object

4. verbal – expressed in spoken words

5. written – expressed in writing

6. print – clearly written text

7. language – a structured system of words or signs for communication

8. hieroglyphics – an ancient system of writing

C. 1. Television
   2. radios
   3. paintings
   4. letter
   5. newspaper
   6. phone
   7. Internet
   8. e-mail
   9. photograph
   10. magazines

D. 1. painting – paintbrush
   2. texting – cell phone
   3. news – newspaper
   4. writing – pen
   5. e-mail – computer

E.   (Individual writing)

13   Genre Words

A. A: biography
   B: fable
   C: mystery
   D: myth
   E: poetry
   F: manual
   G: autobiography
   H: fairy tale
   I: science fiction

   1. C   2. I
   3. G   4. H
   5. F   6. A
   7. B   8. D
   9. E

B.   fantasy ; comics ; history ;
     cookbook ; atlas ;
     horror ; travel ; romance

C.   Fiction:
     comics, fable, fairy tale, fantasy, horror, mystery,
     myth, romance, science fiction
     Non-fiction:
     atlas, autobiography, biography, cookbook,
     history, manual, travel

14   Fashion Words

A.

B. 1. Clothing
   2. Accessory
   3. Fashion Show
   4. Professional

C. 1. accessories
   2. designer ; wardrobe
   3. embellished
   4. fabric
   5. trends
   6. attire
   7. cosmetics
   8. casual
   9. model ; catwalk

D. 1. You should put on a jacket before going
      outside.
   2. Diana put everything in her handbag and left
      for work.
   3. Eshaal wore a gown to the dance at her
      school.
   4. Kingsley could not find his favourite blue jeans.
   5. Harry gave his mom a necklace for her
      birthday.

Review 3

A. 1. cliff
   2. fireplace
   3. baseball
   4. personality trait
   5. caring
   6. influenza
   7. cyclone
   8. telescope
   9. agonized
   10. leopard
   11. stalk
   12. manatee
   13. vaccine
   14. body aches
   15. epidemic
   16. clippers
   17. excavate, classify, analyze
   18. syllable
   19. autobiography
   20. wristwatch

B. Fire Word:
   extinguish ; flammable ;
   crackle ; ignite
   Nature Word:
   boulder ; glacial ;
   brook ; landscape

C. 1. goal
   2. rookie
   3. gymnastics
   4. defenseman
   5. records
   6. skiing
   7. tennis

D.

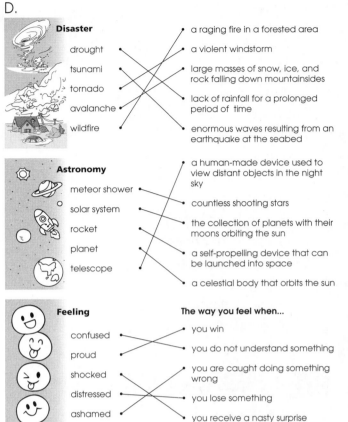

E. Circle in red:
   tiger ; cheetah ; cougar ; lynx ; leopard ; cat ;
   Siamese cat ; purr ; chatter ; felines ; cat
   Circle in blue:
   near threatened ; beluga ; narwhal ; giant
   tortoise ; vulnerable ; endangered ;
   blue whale ; chimpanzee

F. 1. symptoms   2. cough
   3. runny nose   4. medicine
   5. flu   6. archaeologist
   7. historical   8. excavated
   9. civilizations   10. artifacts

G.

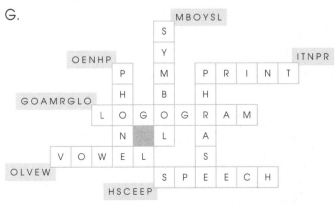

H. Genre: mystery ; fairy tale ; horror ; science fiction
   Fashion: purse ; jeans ; outfit ; fabric

1 Fortune Telling Newspaper

A. 1. eleven years old
2. Mr. Yee
3. WELCOME BACK SUMMER
4. a garbage truck
B. 1. play
2. Jake thinks that it seems weird that the phrase written on Mr. Yee's shirt confirms the headline in the newspaper.
3. Jake thinks it is a coincidence that the newspaper's headlines seem to come true.
4. (Individual answer)
C. (Check 1, 2, 5, 6, 8, 9, 11, and 12.)
D. (Individual writing)
E. (Individual writing)

2 The Myth of Daedalus and Icarus

A. 1. the prince of Athens
2. Daedalus
3. string, feathers, and wax
4. vain
B. 1. The purpose of this myth is to set moral standards and explain how the Icarian Sea got its name.
2. The Labyrinth is a maze built by Daedalus on King Minos's request. It is used to contain a Minotaur.
3. Daedalus warns Icarus that if he flies too high in the sky, the sun will melt the wax in his wings.
4. (Suggested answer)
The myth teaches us not to be vain and reckless.
C. (Individual writing)
D. (Individual writing and drawing)

3 Aladdin

A. 1. spins cotton   2. he is poor
3. a sorcerer   4. two
B. (Suggested answer)
1. He agrees to work for the tradesman because he needs to earn a living and he does not know the tradesman is a wicked sorcerer.
2. He accidentally rubs the enchanted ring and asks the genie who appears as a result of this to help him out.
3. (Suggested answer)
The main problem is that Aladdin is poor. The solution is that the magic ring and lamp bring forth genies who grant Aladdin wishes which make him prosperous.
C. Good Characters:
Aladdin ; Aladdin's mother ; the genie of the ring ; the genie of the lamp ; the princess
Evil Character: the sorcerer
Setting: a cave ; a palace
Events: (Suggested answer)
Aladdin is tricked into working for a tradesman who is really a sorcerer. He gives Aladdin a magic ring and sends him to a dark cave to retrieve a magic oil lamp. Aladdin returns home with the help of the genie of the magic ring. With the help of the genie of the oil lamp, Aladdin becomes rich and marries the princess. The sorcerer tricks her into selling him the magic lamp and takes away all of Aladdin's riches as well as the princess. The genie of the ring helps Aladdin get the lamp back. He is reunited with the princess, and gets back his riches and his palace. Aladdin and the princess live happily ever after.
D. (Check these characteristics.)
passed down through generations ;
begins with "Once upon a time" or "Long ago" ;
contains a problem and solution ;
has a happy ending ;
evil is punished ;
includes magical elements
E. (Individual writing)

4	**Power for Sale**

A. 1. two
   2. past
   3. hope, beauty, and power
   4. paintings
B. 1. It is a fairy tale.
   2. They come up with an idea to sell pebbles that promise things like power, luck, courage, and beauty to become rich.
   3. Frieda notices her pebble is lost and realizes she could not have been getting her energy from it after all.
   4. The gnomes realize their mistakes and make magnificent paintings to sell instead of pebbles.
C. Title: Power for Sale
   Characters
   Hero: Frieda
   Villain: two gnomes
   Setting
   Time: April Fool's Day
   Place: the realm of gnomes and fairies
   Problem (Suggested answer)
   The two gnomes sell pebbles with fake promises of things like energy and luck to the fairies.
   Solution (Suggested answer)
   Frieda and the fairies confront the gnomes. They realize their mistakes and start making and selling magnificent paintings instead of pebbles.
   Events (Suggested answer)
   A tired fairy, Frieda, is tricked into buying pebbles from two mischievous gnomes who promise that the pebbles will bring her energy. They trick other fairies too. Frieda realizes she has been tricked. She and the other fairies confront the gnomes. They stop selling pebbles and start making and selling paintings instead.
D. (Individual writing and drawing)

5	**Summer List**

A. 1. summer activities
   2. at the park
   3. the fishing rod
   4. rides
B. 1. (Suggested answer)
      fist – list ; swing – sting ; wish – fish ; see – tree
   2. (Suggested answer)
      by a sea of flowers ;
      a grumpy bee was annoyed ;
      Now it swims happily with the fish ;
      It's sturdy. It's tall.
   3. The writer gets stung by a bee.
      The writer drops his fishing rod in the water.
      The writer is not tall enough for the rides at the fair.
      The writer does not know how to get down from the tall tree.
C. 1. (Check these characteristics.)
      written in stanzas ; shows the poet's feelings ;
      contains imagery ; contains rhyming words
   2. (Suggested answers)
      fall – all
      sleeves – leaves
      I – fly
      Halloween – queen
   3. (Suggested examples)
      the colourful blanket of leaves ;
      Make carefree kites to fly
D. (Individual writing and drawing)

6	**Marilyn Bell**

A. 1. in Lake Ontario
   2. by 6:00 a.m.
   3. Gus Ryder
   4. through radio stations
   5. terrific

B. 1. magazine article
2. It rained through the night and the water was cold and choppy. Also, Bell faced boredom as her biggest difficulty.
3. She was awarded the prize money by CNE and another $50 000 worth of gifts. Also, she became an instant celebrity and a national treasure.

C. Name of Magazine: Sports Exclusive
Type of Magazine: sports
Headline of Article: Marilyn Bell – Marathon Swimmer
Byline: By Eugene Griffin
Subheadings: Braving Lake Ontario ; Harsh Swimming Conditions ; Our National Treasure
Images: photos
Caption: Marilyn Bell before her feat of swimming in Lake Ontario
Purpose: inform
Target Audience: (Suggested answer)
sports fans, athletes, fans of Marilyn Bell
Other Features: includes a variety of font styles and sizes and a page number

D. (Individual writing and drawing)

7 The History of the Canadian Flag

A. 1. John Cabot
2. in chronological order
3. the Fleur-de-lis
4. in 1965

B. 1. It shows the changes made to the Canadian flag throughout history and the events leading up to its finalization.
2. 4 ; 3 ; 2 ; 1 ; 5
3. The Red Ensign flag is a cross between the Union Jack and a shield bearing the arms of Nova Scotia, Ontario, New Brunswick, and Quebec.

C. Prime Minister (date)
1. Sir John A. Macdonald (July 1, 1867)
2. Alexander Mackenzie (November 7, 1873)
3. Sir John A. Macdonald (October 17, 1878)
4. Sir John Abbott (June 16, 1891)
5. Sir John Thompson (December 5, 1892)
Major Event
(Individual writing)

D. (Individual writing)

8 Think Big!

A. 1. a famous mural
2. on a ceiling
3. difficult
4. colouring the mural

B. 1. It is an informational text.
2. The purpose of this text form is to instruct.
3. (Check these characteristics.)
numbers to show order ; simple and clear language ; imperative sentences ; step-by-step instructions ; helpful illustrations ; list ; heading ; subheadings

C. (Individual writing)

D. (Individual writing and drawing)

9 The Amazing Helen Keller

A. 1. in 1880
2. in Alabama, USA
3. a teacher
4. foreign language

B. 1. flow diagram
    2. Helen became an unruly child due to the frustration of not being able to communicate.
    3. She began to understand and communicate using the tapped code created by Sullivan.
    4. Helen graduated from Radcliffe College with honours, specializing in foreign language and philosophy.
C. 1. Hellen Keller's Milestones and Achievements
    2. title ; graphic boxes ; arrows ; pictures
    3. The events are arranged in chronological order.
    4. Arrows are used to show the order of events.
    5. A timeline is not ideal because there is no information about the dates of many events.
D. (Individual writing)
E. (Individual drawing and writing)

10   Bigfoot Sighting

A. 1. Run for Fun
    2. on April 1, 2019
    3. behind the bushes
    4. the owner of The Shoe Fool
B. 1. It is a newspaper article.
    2. It is non-fiction because it reports an event that took place and includes dates, facts, and quotes.
    3. The purpose of this text is to inform.
    4. The unexpected surprise for some participants was seeing a huge, furry creature with very large feet near the finish line.
    5. He said this because he thinks the possibility of spotting the creature will make people want to participate in the run.
C. 1. The Sunshine News
    2. April 4, 2019
    3. Bigfoot Sighting at Annual Race
    4. By May Flower
    5. 1
    6. 2 to 7
    7. A huge, furry creature was reported near the finish line.

8. By Anna: "Someone was having fun in a big monkey suit. Honestly, his feet were so big he couldn't walk properly."
    By Murphy: "Keep your children and pets inside...At least until we get this sorted out."
D. (Individual writing)
E. (Individual writing and drawing)

11   The Volcano

A. 1. crust
    2. around the mouth
    3. molten rock
    4. geothermal activity
B. 1. encyclopedia entry
    2. (Suggested answer)
        The features include heading, entry, subheadings, diagram, and labels.
    3. The hot lava that erupts from the Earth's surface spreads over a wide area. Many layers of it form the shape of a mountain, which is a volcano.
    4. active volcano:
        a volcano that has erupted at least once in the past 10 000 years
        (Individual example)

        dormant volcano:
        a volcano that is capable of erupting but has not erupted in the past 10 000 years
        (Individual example)
C. 1. volcano
    2. Formation, Types
    3. Structure of a Volcano
    4. Crater ; Lava ; Side Vent ; Ash and Cinders ; Central Vent ; Crust ; Magma Chamber
    5. (Suggested answer)
        This entry would be near the end of the book because "volcano" starts with a "v" and an encyclopedia is arranged in alphabetical order.
D. (Individual writing)
E. (Individual writing and drawing)

12 Canada's Minimum Wage

A. 1. Alberta
   2. average minimum wage
   3. NS and PEI
   4. $11.00

B. 1. The title of the map is "Canada's Hourly Minimum Wage by Province".
   2. The title of the graph is "Hourly Minimum Wage by Province in Canada (2018)".
   3. Nova Scotia has the lowest minimum wage.
   4. $11.00 to $15.00
   5. (Individual answer)

C.

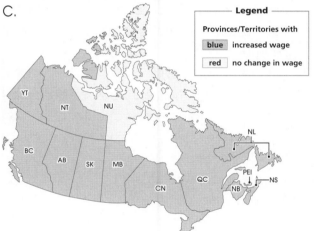

1. Name of the Book: Canadian Atlas
   Title of the Table:
   Hourly Minimum Wage in Canada
   Title of the Map:
   The Change in Hourly Minimum Wage in Canada (April 2017 – April 2018)

2. (Suggested answers)
   Legend: The legend shows which provinces and territories had an increase in the minimum wage, and which had no change in the minimum wage.
   Table: The table lists the minimum wage in each province and territory in both April 2017 and April 2018 to show the difference.
   Colours: The colours visually depict which provinces and territories had an increase in the minimum wage and which had no change.

D. (Individual map and colouring)

13 I Can't Play

A. 1. soccer
   2. her ankle
   3. a technician
   4. defender

B. 1. Melinda is the sender of the e-mail.
   2. Cayenne is the recipient of the e-mail.
   3. (Individual answer)
   4. Melinda was hurt as she ran to save her younger brother from falling off the sofa.
   5. The doctor advised Melinda to get a lot of rest for a few days.
   6. This e-mail is informal because it is written to a friend and uses informal language which includes contractions.

C. 1. Cayenne ; Melinda
   2. melinda@smart.com
   3. Get well soon
   4. three ; 1.jpg ; 2.jpg ; 3.jpg
   5. informal
   Examples: (Suggested answer)
   "Hi Melinda," ;
   contractions such as "I'm" and "you'll" ;
   informal phrases such as "feel like part of the action,"

D. (Individual writing)

14 Sunrise Paradise

A. 1. a service
   2. a resort
   3. by a beach
   4. a customer service representative

B. 1. The purpose of this text is to promote Sunrise Paradise Resort.
   2. Children can play at the Trampoline Palace, play water polo in the pool, watch movies in the theatre, or make sandcastles on the beach.
   3. Birthdays, weddings, and other special events can be hosted at Sunrise Paradise.
   4. (Individual answer)

C. 1. Sunrise Paradise Getaway
   2. Your Home Away from Home!
   3. Activities ; Events ; Contact Us
   4. photos ; logo ; large bold font
   5. in the present tense ; in the future tense ; uses imperatives
   6. company's name ; company's address ; contact information
   7. 416-XXX-XXXX ; paradise@smart.com ; sunriseparadise.smart.ca

D. (Individual writing and drawing)

Review 4

A. 1. label
   2. entertain
   3. myth
   4. a folk tale
   5. includes factual information
   6. descriptive language
   7. a caption
   8. includes a happy ending
   9. graphic
   10. chronological order
   11. step-by-step instructions
   12. a graphic organizer
   13. title, graphic boxes, and arrows
   14. the name of the writer
   15. directly below a photo
   16. labels, diagrams, and subheadings
   17. information about a map
   18. graphs and maps
   19. A picture
   20. their logo

B. 1. F
   2. F
   3. T
   4. T
   5. F
   6. T
   7. T

C. 1. It is a newspaper article.
   2. Name of Newspaper: The Sunshine News
      Date: July 22, 2018
      Headline: Man Rescued by *Voyage II*
      Byline: By Anthony de Luca
      Photo Caption:
      The captain and crew of *Voyage II* rescuing a passenger
      Quote by the Captain:
      "*Voyage II* was scheduled to visit six Caribbean islands in seven days at sea."
   3. The purpose of this text is to inform.
   4. (Suggested answer)
      Mrs. Sue said this because she was grateful for the captain and crew's immediate rescue of Mr. Sue.
   5. (Suggested answer)
      The article will benefit the cruise line because it shows the cruise line cares about its customers and puts their safety first, and it is capable of handling emergencies.

D. Text Type: encyclopedia entry
   Entry: cruise ship
   Diagram Title: Features of a Cruise Ship
   Subheadings: Origins ; Developments

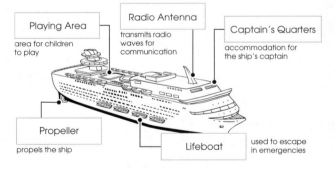

Playing Area
area for children to play

Radio Antenna
transmits radio waves for communication

Captain's Quarters
accommodation for the ship's captain

Propeller
propels the ship

Lifeboat

used to escape in emergencies

E. (Individual writing and drawing)

1.

b	s	s											v	v	b
a	o	o											o	o	a
s	c	c											l	l	d
k	c	c											l	t	m
e	q	e	a	u	c	q	f	x	c	c	j	o	d	e	i
t	e	r	u	o	c	k	e	s	h	o	c	k	e	y	n
b	a	s	e	b	a	l	l	k	c	i	v	g	u	b	t
a	s	k	p	o	b	a	s	i	e	b	a	l	s	a	o
l	t	a	l	w	b	t	s	i	r	k	l	g	o	l	f	n
l	i	t	g	l	k	t	e	n	n	i	s	m	o	l	m
p	q	i	s	i	t	e	n	g	n	i	f	s	q	n	e	f
s	k	n	i	n	i	n	g	b	o	w	t	i	n	g	t	p
t	a	g	n	g	r	w	f	o	o	l	b	o	x	i	n	g

2. dime ; dome ; dove ; love

3. Sail your boat to the lighthouse.
   Then go to Dinosaur Island.
   Finally, sail straight to the treasure.

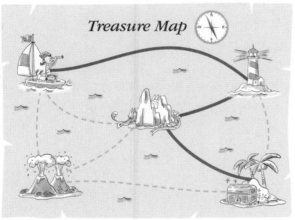

Treasure Map

4. heap ; heat ; heal ; seal ; sell ; well

5.

b	u	t	t	e	b	e	c	w	w	q	q	s	u	p	y
b	a	s	k	c	i	c	a	d	a	u	r	w	v	z	n
e	t	b	a	r	q	b	m	o	s	q	u	i	t	o	e
t	l	l	n	i	u	s	a	a	p	c	c	q	t	x	b
e	a	t	i	c	i	a	n	s	b	r	o	a	e	c	e
p	d	y	r	k	t	u	t	b	e	i	c	a	n	r	q
e	y	e	l	e	o	e	i	e	e	c	k	l	t	o	b
u	b	x	o	t	m	o	s	e	t	k	r	e	a	a	u
e	u	o	c	u	s	t	s	t	l	e	o	o	b	c	m
s	g	b	u	m	b	l	e	b	e	e	a	c	y	z	b
i	u	e	s	b	e	c	m	o	q	t	c	u	b	g	l
i	t	e	t	t	m	o	t	m	o	t	h	s	u	s	e
a	n	s	b	a	n	t	b								
e	c	c	a	u	s	e	e								
e	y	d	o	b	o	n	b								

6.

① house + boat
   ♥ houseboat
   ◇ homeboat

② book + worm
   ☆ storyworm
   ☾ bookworm

③ tea + cup
   ⊙ teapot
   ✉ teacup

④ shiny + fish
   ⬠ shinyfish
   Y starfish

⑤ fire + bug
   △ firebug
   Ψ firefly

7.

a	h	s	o	i	l	s	u	n	r	u	s	p	a	d	e
t	s	t	t	v	i	b	a	s	e	t	e	r	u	b	p
h	a	r	v	e	s	t	a	g	f	l	o	w	e	r	t
i	t	a	h	e	t	i	r	r	a	m	r	e	f	e	i
h	a	w	a	f	e	n	c	e	n	a	a	l	e	a	c
r	o	o	t	t	m	n	e	r	a	w	a	g	o	n	t
g	r	e	e	n	h	o	u	s	e	p	r	o	p	u	u
t	a	i	t	c	a	t	s	e	e	h	e	c	e	t	r
a	c	c	a	b	b	a	g	e	t	n	r	a	k	e	e
s	a	s	a	m	h	e	t	d	h	p	t	r	a	t	o
e			c	c	o	m	p	o	s	t	f	r	n	t	h
		e	s	u	s	l	f	f	e	o	d	e	f		
			e	l	i	s	h	e	d	t	a	o	m		
			m	w	l	e	a	v	e	s	u	n	t		
			r	y	d	o	b	o	n	s	e	h	i		

8.

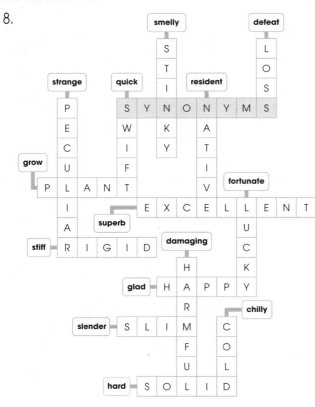

9. (Colour): I ; found ; the ; jewels ; !
   I found the jewels!

10.

11.

12.1. pasta
   2. butter
   3. cake
   4. cream
   5. cheese
   6. soup

13. This message is for the little mermaid who saved my life at sea. Thank you for your kindness. Regards,

Language Games

1 Circle 12 sport words in the word search.

I like sports.

b	s	s
a	o	o
s	c	c
k	c	c

e	q	e	a	u	c	q	f	x	c	c	j	o	d	e	e	i
t	e	r	u	o	c	k	e	s	h	o	c	k	e	y	y	n
b	a	s	e	b	a	l	l	k	c	i	v	g	u	b	b	t
a	s	k	p	o	b	a	s	i	e	b	a	l	s	a	a	o
l	t	a	l	w	b	t	s	i	r	k	l	g	o	l	f	n
l	i	t	g	l	k	t	e	n	n	i	s	m	o	l	l	m
p	q	i	s	i	t	e	n	g	n	i	f	s	q	n	e	f
s	k	n	i	n	j	n	g	b	o	w	t	i	n	g	t	p
t	a	g	n	g	r	w	f	o	o	l	b	o	x	i	n	g

v	v	b
o	o	a
l	l	d
l	t	m

2 Change only one letter at a time to show how the fairy changed "lime" to "love" for the princess's birthday.

| l | i | m | e |

| | i | m | e |

3

Unscramble the letters to find the treasure. Then trace the correct route to bring Polly to the treasure.

STEPS

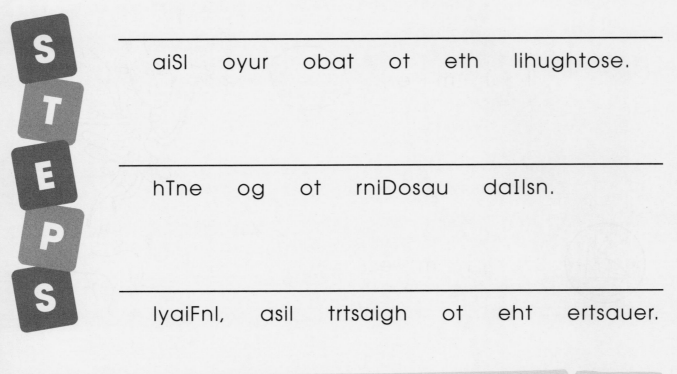

aiSl   oyur   obat   ot   eth   lihughtose.

hTne   og   ot   rniDosau   daIlsn.

lyaiFnl,   asil   trtsaigh   ot   eht   ertsauer.

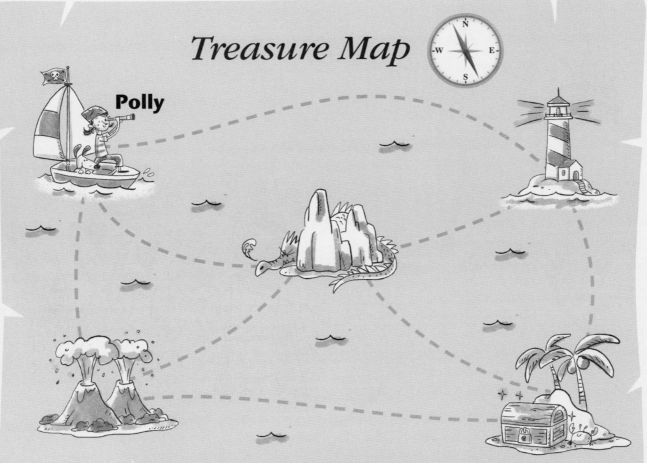

Treasure Map

Polly

4 Change only one letter at a time to show how Sam the Scientist turned "reap" into "well".

5 Circle 12 insect words in the word search.

b	u	t	t	e	b	e	c	w	w	q	q	s	u	p	y
b	a	s	k	c	i	c	a	d	a	u	r	w	v	z	n
e	t	b	a	r	q	b	m	o	s	q	u	i	t	o	e
t	l	l	n	j	u	s	a	a	p	c	c	q	t	x	b
e	a	t	i	c	i	a	n	s	b	r	o	a	e	c	e
p	d	y	r	k	t	u	t	b	e	i	c	a	n	r	q
e	y	e	l	e	o	e	i	e	e	c	k	l	t	o	b
u	b	x	o	t	m	o	s	e	t	k	r	e	a	a	u
e	u	o	c	u	s	t	s	t	l	e	o	o	b	c	m
s	g	b	u	m	b	l	e	b	e	e	a	c	y	z	b
i	u	e	s	b	e	c	m	o	q	t	c	u	b	g	l
i	t	e	t	t	m	o	t	m	o	t	h	s	u	s	e
a	n	s	b	a	n	t	b								
e	c	c	a	u	s	e	e								
e	y	d	o	b	o	n	b								

6 Look at the pictures. Colour the correct codes to show the compound words. Then draw the codes in the boxes to help Eric open the lock.

1. ♥ houseboat
   ◇ homeboat

2. ☆ storyworm
   ☾ bookworm

3. ◎ teapot
   ✉ teacup

4. ⬠ shinyfish
   Y starfish

5. ⌃ firebug
   Ⴤ firefly

7 **Circle 18 gardening words in the word search.**

a	h	s	o	i	l	s	u	n	r	u	s	p	a	d	e
t	s	t	t	v	i	b	a	s	e	t	e	r	u	b	p
h	a	r	v	e	s	t	a	g	f	l	o	w	e	r	t
i	t	a	h	e	t	i	r	r	a	m	r	e	f	e	i
h	a	w	a	f	e	n	c	e	n	a	a	l	e	a	c
r	o	o	t	t	m	n	e	r	a	w	a	g	o	n	t
g	r	e	e	n	h	o	u	s	e	p	r	o	p	u	u
t	a	i	t	c	a	t	s	e	e	h	e	c	e	t	r
a	c	c	a	b	b	a	g	e	t	n	r	a	k	e	e
s	a	s	a	m	h	e	t	d	h	p	t	r	a	t	o
e			c	c	o	m	p	o	s	t	f	r	n	t	h
			e	s	u	s	l	f	f	e	o	d	e	f
			e	l	i	s	h	e	d	t	a	o	m
			m	w	l	e	a	v	e	s	u	n	t
			r	y	d	o	b	o	n	s	e	h	i

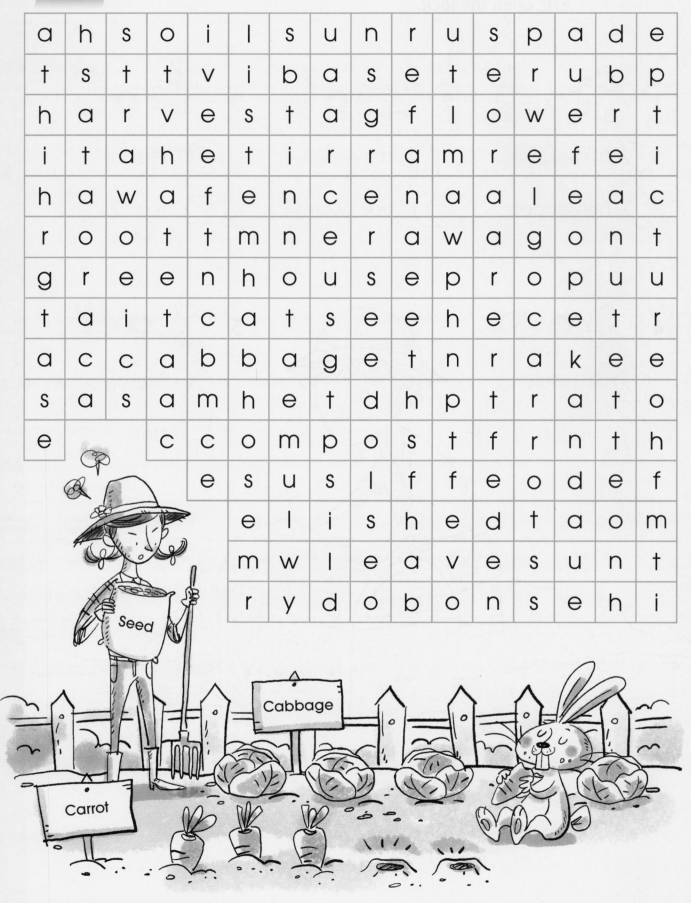

Seed

Cabbage

Carrot

8

Complete the crossword puzzle with synonyms of the clue words.

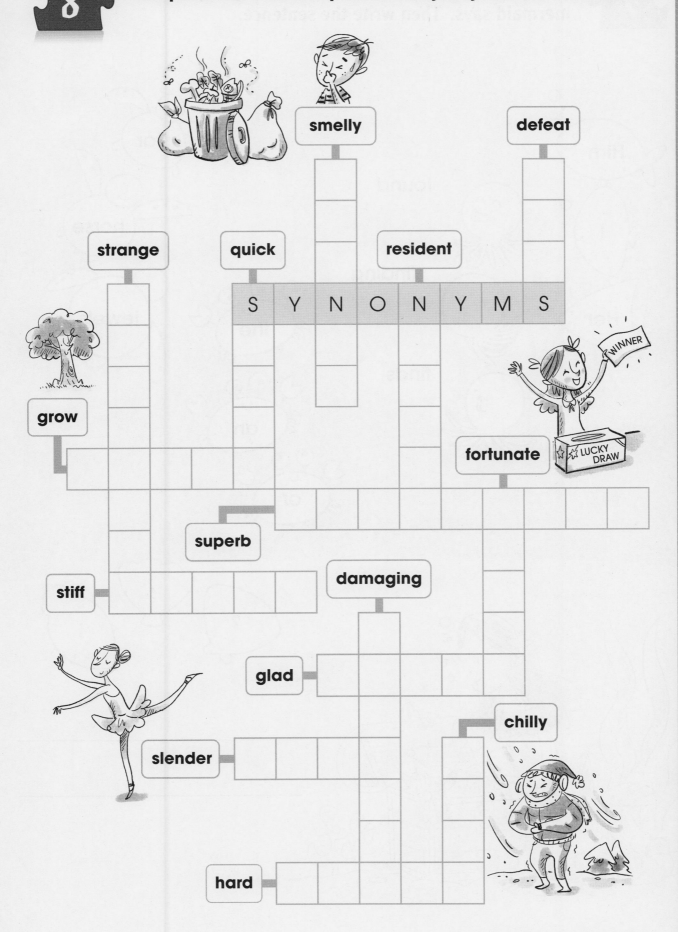

smelly

defeat

strange

quick

resident

S Y N O N Y M S

grow

fortunate

superb

stiff

damaging

glad

chilly

slender

hard

9 Colour the correct sea creature in each group to find out what the mermaid says. Then write the sentence.

10 Trace the correct path following the words that rhyme with "seed" to bring Farmer Al to his farm.

11   Circle 11 Halloween words in the word search.

Halloween
Word Search

```
            c i
            a s
  s s i w o r c a u l d r a
  i c c o s t q m e s t e p p g
  o o y d b w i t c h k a u u s e
  j h s n o o w i f c z m t m n u e
  d c t s o h g h o s t o o p p r p
  i n u i h g t r f t r i c k k a m k
  g w m r e o h e e r t r e i i e r e
  q e e H a l l o w e e n h n z s i t
  c s e s p i d e a a t i b b a k o f
  t q s p i d e r g t k e a l e t n
  p e k e d q s k e l e t o n a o
    r c a n d i e s p t h w a
    s j c a n p i e a
```

12

Find out the food words by breaking the codes. Then write them on the food list.

I need these food items for tonight's dinner.

My Food List

1. _____

2. _____

3. _____

4. _____

5. _____

6. _____

1. 🪣 – il + ⭐ – r

2. 🦋 – 🐝

3. 🐱 – t + 🪁 – it

4. 🐄 – ow + r + 🫖 – st

5. 🪑 – air + 🐑 – shp + 🍟 – frie + e

6. s + 🍊 – range + ☕ – c

13 Unscramble the letters to find out what the message in the bottle says.

Message in the Bottle

ihTs   esemsag   si   ofr   hte   tiltle   remaidm

hwo   asvde   ym   ilfe   ta   esa.

hTank   uoy   rfo   oyur   ikndesns.

aeRdgrs,

_____

_____

_____

_____

_____

Amy

Language Game

Challenge

We have an exciting Language Game Design Challenge! Submit your design to win a prize if your entry is selected and posted on our website!

Entry Rules:

- You have a passion for learning English.
- *Complete EnglishSmart* is your favourite learning tool.
- You are between 6 and 14 years old.

How to Enter:

1. Use the back of this page to create your own language game.
2. Give your language game a title.
3. Make sure the language game is fun!

My Contact Information

Name: _____ Age: _____

School: _____ Grade: _____

E-mail: _____

Parent's Signature

Scan and e-mail this form and your language game to: *ca-info@popularworld.com* or mail it to: 15 Wertheim Court, Units 602-603, Richmond Hill, Ontario, Canada L4B 3H7.